# *is man predictable?*

Biologist P. B. Medawar points out in his provocative book that mankind is always in a state of alarm over a diminishing population or in an even greater state of alarm over an expanding population.

Learned men are either heralding the miraculous advance of modern medicine, or darkly suggesting that the total effect of such a humanistic science will be to perpetuate the weak at the expense of the fit.

Both citizens and educators worry about a declining intelligence level; yet the general populace has never before been so well educated.

Which way is man, the intelligent social animal, headed—toward a bright future or toward extinction? There are impassioned advocates on both sides of this burning question, therefore the cool reason of a biologist's viewpoint is both soothing and stimulating to the interested reader. Without deliberating on philosophical issues, the author implies them with a deft assertion of the facts. Man has evolved to his present state through a fantastically complex genetic history . . . and Professor Medawar claims in these lively essays that the clues to man's future must lie in his essential biology.

# the future of man

by P. B. MEDAWAR

*A MENTOR BOOK*
PUBLISHED BY THE NEW AMERICAN LIBRARY

*Published as a MENTOR BOOK*
*By Arrangement with Basic Books, Inc.*

FIRST PRINTING, SEPTEMBER, 1961

MENTOR TRADEMARK REG. U.S. PAT. OFF. AND FOREIGN COUNTRIES
REGISTERED TRADEMARK—MARCA REGISTRADA
HECHO EN CHICAGO, U.S.A.

*MENTOR BOOKS are published by*
*The New American Library of World Literature, Inc.*
*501 Madison Avenue, New York 22, New York*

PRINTED IN THE UNITED STATES OF AMERICA

*to my mother*

# *contents*

# *introduction*

Lectures of this kind may be either written up or written down. Like most of my predecessors in the BBC's Reith Lecturership, I have chosen the latter course, and what may be read here (with a few trivial alterations) is what I actually said during the broadcasts on Sunday evenings in the winter of 1959. The *Notes,* addressed to a professional audience, are gathered together at the end of the text; I felt that if they were in the text itself they would interrupt the flow of the arguments.

No one need be ashamed of his shortcomings as a "human biologist." A human biologist must be demographer, geneticist, anthropologist, historian, psychologist, and sociologist all in one, and much else besides; he must also be a fairly reasonable sort of human being; and no one can be all of these things. What is written here is therefore the product of a certain combination of knowledge and ignorance; it is also the product of much careful and anxious thought. I can now see a good deal wrong with the style of these lectures—they were too closely reasoned, and often made unfair demands on the listener's attention—but I still feel I was quite right in attempting to expound the processes of reasoning rather than the finished products of thought. Nearly all that follows is unfinished thinking.

I should not myself have been so arrogant as to choose *The Future of Man* as a title for these lectures; but I am glad now that it was proposed to me, because it made me think more widely than I had done before; and this, I believe, was part of the Corporation's intention when it founded the Reith Lecturership. But lest there should be any possible misunderstanding of my pretensions, let me say for a second time what I said in my first lecture: answers to questions of the kind I propound here are deeply necessary for an understanding of the future of man; but they are not sufficient.

In the preparation of these lectures I have pestered my professional colleagues mercilessly: among the many I have turned to for advice—either before the lectures were delivered or in the preparation of the notes—are Dr. John Fraser Roberts, Dr. H. Kalmus, Professor Karl Popper, Professor Kenneth Mather, Dr. J. D. Tanner, Professor P. L. Krohn, Mr. R. B. Freeman, Sir Stewart Duke-Elder, Dr. J. Hajnal, Dr. A. Comfort, and many others, including the members of this Department: I am deeply grateful to them for their good advice. Two of my closest colleagues, Professor David Newth and Mr. John Maynard Smith, read every lecture in draft. They managed both to criticize them with the candour one longs for on these occasions and to make me feel confident that what I had to say was worth saying. To them I am grateful above all; but I must make it clear that mistakes of fact or errors of judgment are mine alone. And I join with my predecessor, Professor A. C. B. Lovell, in thanking and complimenting our producer, Mr. J. Weltman, not merely for the many skilful touches that helped to make the lectures more intelligible than they otherwise would have been (nor even for his lessons in the art of reading aloud!); but for his entire grasp of and sympathy for what I was trying to do.

P. B. M.

Department of Zoology
University College, London
December 31, 1959

# 1.

## *the fallibility of prediction*

The best way to give you an idea of the subject of these Reith Lectures is to put before you some of the questions I am hoping to answer, and this I shall do in a minute or two's time; but, first of all, for my own peace of mind, I should like to explain some of the uncertainties I have felt about their style and general purpose.

I first thought of attempting a grand prophetic statement about Man's future as *Homo sapiens*— of doing for biology something of the kind that physicists have done when they have written about the shape of the foreseeable future or of what might happen in the next million years; but I soon saw that if I were to attempt anything of the kind on behalf of biology, I should be obliged either to weary you with endless qualifications and reservations and disclaimers, or else to try to disguise the thinness of the reasoning by taking refuge in apocalyptic prose. The effect of the first procedure is to leave people perplexed about what the lecturer is actually saying, supposing he has screwed himself up to the point of saying anything at all; and of the second, to make them doubtful about his reasoning, stirring though what he said may well have been.

The more deeply I studied the problems I am going to talk about, the more deeply I became convinced that the opinions of the learned are often much less interesting than the reasoning which professes to uphold them; and in the outcome I decided that these lectures were to be about the *process of foretelling* rather than about what is actually foretold. The decision was almost forced upon me by the fact that some of the problems I shall discuss are very controversial. For example, I shall explain in a later lecture why some experts (who at the moment have gone into hibernation) declare that the average intelligence of Englishmen is almost certainly declining, and why other experts are almost sure that it is not. I shall take sides, because one opinion does seem to me to be weightier than the other; but what I shall *not* do is to discuss the consequences of any fall of intelligence.

Again, I shall put to you the purely theoretical problem of the limits of physical and intellectual improvement. Some biologists believe that, apart from certain recurrent accidents, a population can become uniform in all kinds of desirable "inborn" qualities, and can maintain itself in that state of uniform excellence according to the simple formula that like begets like. Other biologists are inclined to think that inborn diversity or inequality is a necessary part of the texture of human populations, and that it is kept in being by means which are often incompatible with "breeding true." This problem lies at the very centre of eugenics, and I shall do my best to explain the difference of principle on which the argument turns.

In the most general terms, the questions I have in mind are these: can man go on evolving in the future as he has evolved in the past, or is there some good reason why his evolution should now have come to an end? What are the evolutionary forces acting on men today, and how far can we predict their effects? For example, it is often said that advances in medicine and hygiene are undermining the fitness of the human race. It is said, too, that the practice of having fewer children than one is capable of having is so unnatural that it is bound to have evil consequences, not excluding the ultimate extinction of mankind. Are these just gloomy philosophizings, or do they contain the elements of a most unwelcome truth? Is it even possible to predict and regulate the size of human populations, so that we do not start worrying about why the birth-rate is not going up almost as soon as we stop worrying about why it is not going down? This is the problem I shall consider in my present lecture; it is important, and it makes an excellent text for discussing the fallibility of prediction.

In the last of my six lectures I shall turn to still more general questions, and I shall discuss the sense and significance of the belief that man is beginning to evolve in an entirely novel way.

I think that answers to questions of this kind, in so far as it is possible to answer them, are deeply necessary for any understanding of the future of man; and when I say that they are necessary, please remember that I have not said, and do not imply, that they are sufficient. This is all I can say by way of excuse for leaving out so much that is promised by the title these lectures bear. Even so, I cannot hope to be lucky enough to escape the charge that my approach is materialistic. I can neither deny this charge nor admit it, because "materialism" is a word that has lost its power to convey an exact meaning; I can, however, resent it, because it is a word that has not yet lost its power to cause offence. To my mind, "analytical" or "exploratory" would be a better description. But instead of worrying about which word to use, let me give you an illustration of the way in which a particular problem in human biology has been approached.

It has been fairly general experience that the ratio of the births of boys to the births of girls goes up towards the end of or shortly after major wars.[1] The ratio of boys to girls in Great Britain went up after the first world war and again in about the middle of the second. One way to explain this is to say that it represents Nature's attempts to make up for the loss of men. Superior people smile at this explanation, perhaps forgetting that it contains the elements of very good sense. Many natural processes are self-regulating—are so adjusted that they can compensate for the effects of disturbance; war is indeed a disturbance, and we should expect it to bring any such power of self-regulation into force. This is a satisfying explanation because it *classifies* the phenomenon: we feel we now know the kind of thing that has been going on. But it marks the end of a train of thought instead of the beginning of an exploration, and even if it were true—which seems unlikely, if only because the war-time change in the sex ratio occurred in some countries which were not at war—it would still leave us wondering about the means by which the process of self-regulation achieved its effect.

Most attempts to explain the war-time change in the sex ratio treat it as a special case of a much more general phenomenon that has nothing to do with war: the fact that older mothers have relatively fewer boys than younger mothers.[2] How is this more general phenomenon to be explained? The most popular explanation runs as follows. It is a fact that, from birth onwards, boys and men are more fragile or vulnerable than girls or women, in the sense that, whatever their ages may be, their chances of living one more year are, on the average, slightly less. If we now make the rather dubious assumption that this greater fragility of boys is true from conception until birth as well as from birth onwards, then the answer seems clear: for some reason younger mothers provide a better environment in the womb than older mothers. This lessens the slight disadvantage of being a boy baby and so makes it understandable that a higher proportion of boys should survive till birth.

On closer inquiry, however, it turns out that a mother's age, as such, does not account for the general fact that older mothers have relatively fewer boys; in any case, it could not account for the sharp rise in the ratio of new-born boys to new-born girls in Great Britain between 1941 and 1942, because the ages of mothers did not change as they should have changed if this simple explanation were true.

However, this is not the full story. It is true, on the whole, that the children of younger mothers are also earlier children; are first or second children, say, instead of third or fourth; but it is not invariably true, because a woman over thirty might be having her first child while a woman under thirty was having her last. The age of a mother must therefore be distinguished from her *parity,* that is, her rank in terms of the number of children she has already had. Moreover, the children of younger mothers are usually the children of younger fathers, so the father's age must be considered too. As I have said, the most recent work suggests that the age of the mother, as such, has not much to do with the sex ratio of new-born children; the age of the father certainly has, though for unknown reasons; and so, perhaps, has the mother's parity.[3]

During the later years of the war there was a slight increase in the proportion of first and second children and probably a slight decrease in their fathers' ages as well; yet neither change seems to have occurred on a scale that could account for the

alteration in the sex ratio. But although the explanations that have been suggested, and others like
them, turn out to be inadequate, the point is that
this is the *kind* of explanation we should seek.

Let me give one other example of the analytical
method because it illustrates a different point. On
the average, children born between May and October
seem to get slightly higher scores in intelligence tests
than children born from November to April. Is it the
season of conception or birth that somehow affects
the intelligence of children, in so far as these tests
can measure it; or is it the intelligence of the parents
that influences the season of conception of the
child? The second must surely be the explanation:
for example, when one compares the average
scores of winter and summer children who are
brothers or sisters, the difference between them almost completely disappears.[4] If the phenomenon
were not to be analysed in this fashion, there is no
limit to the fancies we might build upon the mere
correlation between intelligence and season of birth;
we might even be tempted to think that the Signs of
the Zodiac had something to do with the matter;
that there must, after all, be something in what
the astrologers say.

I should now like to turn to the deeply important
problem of trying to predict and to regulate the
size of a human population. As I have implied, it is
an instructive paradox that we are usually oppressed either by the fact that the birth-rate is unduly high or by the fact that it is unduly low; and
the world today is such that we can worry about
both at once. For reasons I shall now try to explain, there is not much likelihood that we shall ever
cease to be worried by the one problem or the
other, though we can hope for long periods of respite
in which we need not worry very much. Populations are potentially capable of growing at com-

pound interest, but cannot in fact grow for any great length of time at any net rate of compound interest which is persistently above or below zero.[5] If the rate remains persistently below zero the population will die out (for that is what a negative rate implies); and if the rate stays persistently above zero the population will grow without limit and must eventually starve. No one contests these simple truths; people hold different opinions about the problem of overpopulation, but the differences are about its immediate urgency and about the tactics that should be adopted at this present time. But as my chief concern is with method, with the process of foretelling, I propose to discuss the problems of prediction and analysis that concern Great Britain and, to a greater or lesser degree, the rest of the Western world.

Before the war a number of highly skilled demographers said that if the prevailing patterns of birth-rates and death-rates were to continue then the population of most advanced industrial countries would go down steeply, in a matter of tens of years.[6] They pointed out—what seems obvious now, though it was far from obvious then, even to some biologists—that no comfort was to be got from the fact that the populations of most of these countries were still increasing, because the increase was mainly due to the success of ingenious modern ways of postponing the death of people beyond child-bearing age. As a separate consideration, various forecasts were made of the size of our own population at various intervals up to the year 2000. It is already possible to see that these predictions were systematically mistaken: they were all too low. One of them, putting the population of England and Wales below 30,000,000 in the year 2000, falls short by 20,000,000 of what the Registrar General now thinks of as a likely figure.

Before I discuss the shortcomings of these pre-war

forecasts I do want to make it clear that they were expressly carried out as statistical exercises on the basis of a number of perfectly understandable assumptions, and that it would be a disaster if experts stopped making predictions of this degree of importance merely for fear of being wrong. Moreover, they were a big improvement, in point of method, on some of the forecasts or diagnoses made even a few years before. As late as 1930 an eminent foreign biologist declared that nothing could provide a more sensitive measure of the biological health of a population than the ratio of the annual numbers of births and deaths. When he turned the searchlight of this conception upon Great Britain he found no cause whatsoever for alarm. What makes his judgment so infuriating is that it happened to be more nearly right, in its general tendency, than estimates based upon reasoning incomparably more exact.

I suppose there were three main sources of error in these earlier predictions. The first was lack of information. In spite of its obvious importance, we in Great Britain did not begin to record the ages at which mothers bear their children until 1938, about ninety years after the need for information of this type had been explicitly foreseen; and we still do not record the age of the father. But, more than that, we need to know about the size of families, and how many families there are of each particular size, and how families are successively built up in each year after marriage. If pre-war demographers had had the kind of information that has since been provided by the Family Census of 1946 and the general census of 1951 they would have approached their problems in a different way: indeed, it was because of their insistence that the Family Census of 1946 was carried out.

A second source of error was to place too much confidence in the power of an index like the so-called "net reproduction rate" to measure a population's biological fitness, its power to replace itself from one generation to the next. Not so very long ago a socially conscious person who heard mention of the net reproduction rate at once assumed a grave expression, which showed that he understood its import, and may have been intended to show that he knew exactly what it meant. It is, in fact, a measure of fertility which makes allowance for mortality —which does not assume, as cruder measures do, that everyone is lucky enough to live up to and right through the period of reproduction. It is usually based on the female population only, and only on female births, and it is arrived at by an arithmetic exercise which there is no need to describe.[7] Conceived in just those terms—as a well-defined computation which takes into account both gain by birth and loss by death—it is a good way of summarizing in one figure some of the more important information about the mortality and fertility that happens at that time to be in force. It was perfectly well understood that the computation itself gave one no authority to assume that fertility and mortality would not alter; but, when it is used as a measure of replacement, the net reproduction rate can only be as valid as our reasons are for thinking that fertility and mortality will in fact remain constant.

In real life the net reproduction rate fluctuates far more from year to year than one would expect of any index that professes to be a fundamental measurement of reproductive health. Between 1930 and 1940 the net reproduction rate in America, as in many European countries, was below unity, that is, below the level of exact replacement, one for one. In 1952 it reached the fantastic figure of 1.56, corresponding to growth by compound interest at the rate of 56 per cent per generation; but not even an American population could change in a few years from one whose future was looked at pensively

to one which looked as if it would get completely
out of hand. The net reproduction rate is extremely
sensitive to changes in, for example, the ages at
which women bear their children—to changes
which need not be of great importance when thought
of in terms of the span of a human reproductive life.
But there is a more fundamental objection to using
the net reproduction rate, or any other index like it,
to predict what will happen in years ahead; to make
it clear I must explain what is meant by a "stable"
population.

A population has not merely a size; it has also a
structure; and to describe a population at any moment one must know not only its total number but
how that total is built up of people of every different
age. A "stable" population is so called because it
has a constant or steady age-structure or age-dis-
tribution, one which will not change so long as the
rates of fertility and mortality remain constant. Un-
like any real population I am aware of, it can repro-
duce its structure from one generation to the next,
and even regenerate or restore itself if some up-
heaval like a war or depression should temporarily
change its shape. A stable population grows at a
constant net rate of compound interest which may,
of course, be zero, so that births and deaths cancel
each other, and the population stays constant in
size as well as shape.[8] Stability can be achieved
only if the same age-specific rates of mortality and
fertility have been in force for something like 100
years. No large population has ever achieved such a
stability, and it is not at all likely that it ever will.
This is why students of populations wear censorious
frowns when people talk, as they so often do, of
"stabilizing" the population of the world or of one
country or another at any particular figure they
may have in mind; for, short of tyranny, it is not at
all clear how any such stability could be achieved.

When it is used for predictive purposes, the net

reproduction rate can be thought of as a preview of what the population's rate of increase would eventually come to be if fertility and mortality remained constant long enough for a state of stability to be achieved. But if the population is not stable to begin with (in fact it will not be) then its composition by age and sex will certainly alter—not *in spite of* the fact that fertility remains the same but *because* it remains the same. The assumption that fertility will remain constant therefore implies that the population will change in structure; and these changes, in turn, make it likely—though not logically certain— that fertility itself will change. At the very least they will make us look anew at our reasons for assuming that it would remain constant. The net reproduction rate cannot be used as if we were taking the nation's temperature; as if we were assessing its state of reproductive health. It has yet to be shown that any one index of fertility can be used for such a purpose.

All this sounds very disheartening; but out of the uneasiness and dissatisfaction of demographers a rather different style of analysis has emerged. The matter of principle involved is this. The life of a nation goes on from day to day and from year to year, and the changes that happen, historical changes, are marked against a scale of calendar time. But the lives and livelihoods and reproduction of men and women are marked against years of age, and the natural unit of demographical prediction is not, therefore, a calendar year or a sub-division of a century but a life or a sub-division of a life. The rates of fertility that will prevail here in five years' time will be shaped by today's teenagers, wondering when or whether they will get married; by people in their early twenties having their first children, and by people in their thirties having their later children or their last. Every such group has different experiences behind it and different prospects before it, but the fertility index we compute in five years' time will remain indifferent to them all. Yet it cannot be assumed that those who are twenty in 1965 will have the same fertility as the forty-year-olds had when *they* were twenty; or that they will grow up to have the fertility the forty-year-olds happened to have had in 1965.

The analysis of populations in terms of the changes that occur from one calendar year or decade to another is sometimes called "secular analysis," and obviously it must be reinforced by analysis of a different style: one which takes all the people born in one year or married in one year and follows them through their lives. Analysis of this kind is called "cohort analysis"—it slices time lengthways instead of cutting across it year by year. The adoption of cohort analysis is the most important advance in practical demography of the past ten years.[9] No one pretends that its adoption is an intellectual triumph; as I said, it was mainly lack of information that prevented its coming into use before; but in any empirical sense it has been highly informative and revealing.

Cohort analysis makes it easier to resolve fertility into factors—sex ratio, marriage rates, the ages at which people marry; above all, it has shown how important it is to know the pattern in which married couples build their families. No other method could have shown so clearly that the tremendous increase in the birth-rate which began towards the end of the war was mainly due to a change in the pattern of making families: people began to have in 1942 and 1943 the children they would normally have had two or three years beforehand. The postponement of births need not imply that families are going to be smaller than they otherwise would have been, and need not therefore have very much bearing on the problem of replacement. It is during times such as these, with changes in the rates and ages of marriage and in the pattern of building families, that indices like the net reproduction rate are least informative.

The most striking single fact that has emerged from cohort analysis is the remarkably unwavering trend of the size of completed families. It has fallen smoothly from an average of just over six for couples married in the eighteen-sixties to an average of just over two for those who married in the nineteen-thirties. There is an increasing element of guesswork in estimating the number of children of later marriages because not all of them have yet been born; cohort analysis can never be completely up to date. But there is a stability about the pattern of making families which suggests that forecasts founded upon cohort analysis are going to be nearer the mark than any made before the war.

As for replacement, I do not know that any demographer, on present evidence, now fears a serious decline in the population of Great Britain. The latest estimates suggest that we are just about breaking even; demographers are perhaps temperamentally disinclined to put them higher, if only to correct the illusion that all must now be well because the birth-rate went up so rapidly after the war. There are signs, though, that the most recently married couples are going to have larger families; certainly the marriage rate has been going up and the average age at marriage going down—although this does not imply that people who marry nowadays in their early twenties are going to have families of the same size as those who married in their early twenties before the war. In so far as purely biological pressures can influence marriage rates and ages, I guess that the present upward turn may be genuine and not just temporary. In my next lecture I shall refer to the fact that the average age at which children become sexually mature is still going down. Pressures of this kind may not be strong but they are very insistent; combined with everything that goes with a system of social security they could well increase fertility or, at least, change families to a pattern in which married couples have all the children they intend to have by an earlier age than hitherto. I should not be in the least surprised if in the nineteen-seventies or nineteen-eighties we in Great Britain were to start exchanging uneasy glances about the dangers of over-population, and wondering where things were going to end.

I have been saying that human lives, generation by generation, have a much longer stride than the march of history by calendar years or decades, so that it can be very misleading to assess the reproductive health or future size of a population from the fertility that prevails in any one year or group of years. The advantage of cohort analysis is that it makes it easier to resolve fertility into factors which have a meaning in terms of the way in which people actually behave. Predictions founded upon cohort analysis are somewhat more exact in the sense that one can foresee a little more clearly what follows from one's assumptions; and if these predictions are wrong, as to some extent they surely will be, it will be easier in retrospect to see which assumptions were faulty and which factors changed in unforeseeable ways.[10] This is about all that can be expected of predictions of this degree of complexity, though many biologists and demographers did at one time hope for more—to reveal in the growth of human population the unfolding of grand historical principles with the exigency and thrust of physical laws.

Furthermore, it is a technical error to suppose that in real life one can stabilize a human population, in the sense of bringing it to a state in which it will no longer change as a result of its own internal properties. Short of tyranny, all that can be done in an administrative sense is to coax and warn and bribe a population, to try to prevent its becoming unduly small; and to change these policies, with no sense of inconsistency or grievance, if it thereupon shows signs of becoming unduly large. In other words, policies can be adopted which fall equally far short of tyranny and of *laissez-faire*; they can be energetic and reasonable and effective without claiming to hold good in perpetuity or to be governed by the workings of grand demographic laws. I have a feeling that the same may be true, and true for much the same kind of reason, of other still more complex human affairs.

# 2.

## the meaning of fitness

At the beginning of my first lecture I mentioned some of the questions I was hoping to answer, and among them were these two: Is there any real reason to suppose that advances in medicine and hygiene are undermining the fitness of the human race? And is man potentially capable of further evolution, or must we suppose that his evolution has now come to an end? In the course of trying to answer these questions I shall be obliged to use the words "fitness," "inheritance," and "evolution," but to use them in narrow or unfamiliar ways. Scientists do sometimes tend to *brandish* these special usages at the layman, as if they had a sort of inner rightness; but it would be more gracious, and would reveal a better sense of language, if they apologized for them or explained them away.

In everyday speech "fitness" means suitability or adaptedness or being in good condition; "evolution" means gradual change, with the connotation of unfolding; and as for "inheritance," we may hope to inherit money, rights, or property; we might inherit, too, a mother's eyes or a grandfather's gift for fiddling. These are the meanings (there is no need to say the "proper" meanings) of fitness, evolution, and inheritance—the meanings for which scientists chose them when they were struggling to put their conceptions into words. In the course of time those conceptions have become clearer—more choosy, if you like—but the words which embody them have remained the same. The change that has gone on is sometimes described by saying that scientists give the meanings of words a new precision and refinement: a fair statement, were it not for the implication that they extract the true or pure meaning from crude ore. The innocent belief that words have an essential or inward meaning can lead to an appalling confusion and waste of time. Let us take it that our business is to attach words to ideas and definitions, not to attach definitions to words.[1]

The idea scientists now have in mind when they speak of "fitness" can be explained like this. All the people alive 100 years from now will be our descendants, but not all of us will be their ancestors. In retrospect, therefore, it will be possible to give us scores or marks according to the share we took in being the ancestors of those future people; and those who took a larger share will be described as fitter than those who took a lesser share. The word "fitness," then, has come to mean *net reproductive advantage,* and students of heredity, geneticists, do not deliberately use it in any other sense. One hears bitter complaints about this newer use of "fitness," because it neglects so much of what is deeply important in human life: for example, the influence of good or evil people who happen to have no children but who are so obviously fit or unfit members of society in everything except this narrow genetic sense. But the contempt we may feel for the word must on no account be transferred to the idea that it embodies, an idea which has a central place in modern evolutionary thought.[2]

The argument that advances in medicine and hygiene are undermining the overall fitness of mankind is based on the belief that there is a hereditary or genetic element in all human ills and disabilities, even if it amounts to no more than a predisposition. This is known to be true of some diseases and not known to be false of any, so there can be no disagreement here. In its simplest form, the argument then runs as follows: because of the discovery of insulin, antibiotics, and so on, we are preserving for life and reproduction people who even ten years ago might have died. We are therefore preserving the genetically ill-favoured, the hereditary weaklings, who can intermarry with and therefore undermine the constitution of normal people; and as a result of all this, mankind is going downhill.

If by "going downhill" is meant "declining in biological fitness," with the implication that mankind will probably die out, this argument is simply a museum of self-contradictions.[3] It is true that we preserve for life people who even ten years ago might have died; but then we do not live ten years ago: we live today. It is also true that if some disaster were to destroy the great pharmaceutical industries to which diabetics and the victims of Addison's disease literally owe their lives, then a great many of them might die; but what could be deduced from this, except the lunatic inference that people who might conceivably die tomorrow might just as well be dead today? So let me put the argument in a form in which it might be put by a humane and intelligent person. He might say something like this:

I live in a country with a National Health Service, and the effect of this is that, in a sense, I myself suffer from diabetes and rheumatoid arthritis, and so on—from mental deficiency too. Of course my sufferings are only economic, in the sense that it is my taxes that help to pay the bill; but, as a result of them, I can afford to have only two children, though I very much wanted three. Now I am a sound and healthy person, and though I'm all for helping other less lucky people, it is clear that what you call their "biological fitness" is being bought at the expense of mine.

There are two arguments here, and they cannot be considered apart. The first is that people of a genetically sound constitution are being crowded out by the inferior. My spokesman was too humane to resent the idea that the inferior should survive and have children, but he saw some danger in the fact that the population of the future would contain fewer of his descendants because it would contain more of theirs. The second point he makes is that inborn resistance to a disease can be taken as evidence of a *general* soundness of body, of fitness in some rounded and comprehensive sense; so that even if the people he described as unlucky could all be cured of their particular disabilities, there would still be a deep-seated, though hidden, deterioration of mankind.

The arguments I have just outlined are serious and respectable, but they are not generally valid; they may sometimes represent the very opposite of the truth. Consider one of the forms of inborn resistance to a very severe form of malaria, subtertian malaria. It is now known that people can enjoy a definite inborn resistance to subtertian malaria if their red blood corpuscles contain something between 30 and 40 per cent of an unusual form of haemoglobin, haemoglobin S as opposed to haemoglobin A. One of the consequences of possessing haemoglobin S is that the red blood cells tend to collapse if deprived of oxygen; they become

sickle shaped instead of remaining rounded, and
people whose blood behaves in this way are said to
show the "sickle cell trait." Sickle cell trait can be
found in parts of Africa, in some Mediterranean
countries, and in parts of India—always in places
where malaria has been or still is rife. It is not a dis-
abling condition, so its victims should not be said to
"suffer" from it; and, in any event, it confers a high
degree of resistance to the multiplication of the malaria organism in the blood.

This sounds like a splendid example of Nature's
ingenuity in coping with a particularly murderous
disease, malaria, without the help of these new-
fangled drugs; but until one knows the rest of the
story one cannot appreciate how devilishly ingenious it is.

The formation of haemoglobin S instead of A is
due to an inborn difference of a particularly uncompromising kind, in the sense that if a person is genetically qualified to produce haemoglobin S, by
possessing the appropriate "gene" or genetic factor, then he surely will. People who show sickle cell
trait do so because they have inherited the gene
that changes haemoglobin A to S from one, and only
one, of their parents. But when two such people
marry and have children, one quarter of their children, on the average, will inherit that gene from both
their parents; all their haemoglobin, instead of only
part of it, will be of type S; and as a result of this
they usually die early in life of a destructive disease
of the blood known as "sickle cell anaemia." This
highly successful form of inborn resistance to malaria therefore makes it certain that a number of
children will die.

The situation as a whole can be set out in the
form of a balance sheet or equation. In some parts
of the world where malaria is rife, people with
sickle cell trait are the fittest people. Alongside
them are, on the one hand, normal people, whose

haemoglobin is wholly of type A; and, on the other hand, the victims of sickle cell anaemia, whose haemoglobin is wholly of type S. The proportion in which these three classes occur adjusts itself automatically to a pattern in which the loss of life due to malaria and to sickle cell anaemia nicely counterbalances the gain that is due to the greater fitness of those with sickle cell trait. Nevertheless, in malarial regions, populations which possess this genetic structure are fitter than populations which do not.[4]

Essentially the same explanation will account for the widespread occurrence in certain parts of Italy of the disease known as Cooley's anaemia and, not impossibly, for the otherwise paradoxically high incidence of a certain fatal inborn disease of the pancreas [5] in Great Britain and elsewhere. In all such cases it may turn out that there is, or recently has been, some special advantage in having inherited from one parent, and one parent only, the genetical factor which produces such disastrous effects when it is inherited from both.

The moral of this story—though morality seems to have little to do with it—is that mankind will improve if we stamp out inborn resistance to malaria by stamping out malaria itself. Sickle cell anaemia is in fact disappearing from the Negro population of America at about the rate we should expect if malaria had ceased to be a scourge to it 200 or 300 years ago. So the only good thing about inborn resistance to malaria is—inborn resistance to malaria: it does *not* reveal any general soundness of constitution; and this is just the opposite to what my imaginary spokesman supposed. It is simply not true to say that advances in medicine and hygiene must cause a genetical deterioration of mankind. There is more to be feared from a slow decline of human intelligence, but that is a different matter: *if* it is happening, it is because the rather stupid are biologically fitter than those who are innately more intelligent, not because medicine is striving to raise the biological fitness of those who might otherwise be hopelessly unfit.

This question of a possible decline of intelligence is very important, and I shall devote my fifth lecture to it; but, having referred to mind, and defects of mind, it is essential to make this point. Some forms of idiocy and imbecility are congenital. "Congenital" is a vague word, but I use it here to refer to an idiocy which follows from an inborn defect of the genetic make-up as it was laid down at the moment of conception. This defect represents an inborn difference from other people, but it is no more a property of the genetic make-up *as a whole* than the inborn difference between people of blood-groups A and B. One particular form of imbecility, now known as phenylketonuria, is the effect of a single, particular, and accurately identified inborn error of metabolism. In point of inheritance it is essentially similar to another disturbance of metabolism, alkaptonuria, the most serious effect of which is usually no worse than a darkening of the urine after it is exposed to air. To suppose, then, that congenital imbecility pointed to some general inborn inadequacy or degeneracy is nonsense—ignorant and cruel nonsense, too. Our ambition should be to *cure* phenylketonuria, for it is an illusion to suppose that congenital afflictions are necessarily incurable; and if eventually we do cure phenylketonuria, we shall in no sense be conniving at a genetical degradation of mankind.

In a later lecture I shall mention one form of gross mental defect, mongolism, which is by no means so simple in origin as phenylketonuria: it is the result of a damaging genetic accident involving a whole chromosome, and it is not at all easy to see how it might be cured. But it *is* an accident, a particular accident, one which happens more often to the children of older mothers; it is not to be thought of as an outward fulfilment of some inner degeneracy of a family stock.[6] When you come to think of it, all defects of the genetic constitution must have an accidental or unpremeditated or casually intrusive quality—"epiphenomenal" is the word; for it is impossible, indeed self-contradictory, that any animal should have evolved into the possession of some complex and nicely balanced genetic make-up which rendered it unfit. It is this fact that justifies our always hoping to find a cure.

"Inheritance" was the second of the three words of which I said that biologists use them in special or unfamiliar ways. Just what is inherited when geneticists speak of inheritance? It is becoming increasingly popular to say that a child inherits certain genetical *instructions* about how his growth and development are to proceed. This sounds like an ordinary metaphor—very apt, no doubt, but perhaps misleading; but I do not think "metaphor" is quite the word. The idea of genetical instruction has come into use because, under the influence of telephone engineers and higher mathematicians, we now recognize a general, abstract similarity between all kinds of different ways of transmitting information. The passage of genetical instructions from parents to children is a particular concrete example of the more general idea of an act of communication, and just as valid an example of that idea as the information which we transmit in writing, by telephone, or by direct speech.

A gramophone record is a solid object which contains instructions about what particular sounds a reproducing apparatus is to utter. Genetical instructions are also conveyed by solid objects, in this case chromosomes; and the specificity of the instructions—their property of being this instruction and not that—is a specificity of chemical structure: different molecular patterns convey different information, just as different sinuosities of the groves of a record embody instructions about making different sounds. The discovery that nucleic acids are the substances that embody genetical information is to my mind the most important discovery in modern science, but I shall not argue the point because nothing turns on whether you agree with me or not.[7]

Genetical instructions are sometimes strict and uncompromising, in the sense that they can be carried out in one way only, if at all. The nature of one's blood-group or haemoglobin is strictly governed by one's genetic constitution, with little or no opportunity for compromise. But much more often the instructions allow a certain latitude in their execution—we differ from one another partly because we received different genetical instructions from our parents, but partly because, from conception onwards, our surroundings have acted upon us differently, and have therefore affected the way in which those instructions are carried out.

The theory of evolution is a theory which declares that genetical instructions change in character in the course of time. In my first lecture I said that a population had a certain age structure, revealed by classifying its members into groups by age. In the same way a population has a genetic structure, a particular pattern of genetic make-up; just as its members are of many different ages, so also are they of many different genetic kinds. *Evolution* is a change in the genetic structure of a population—but a systematic change, a change with a definite direction or consistent trend.

We have seen such changes happening in our own lifetimes. In many hospitals bacteria have come to resist the action of penicillin, because bacteria genetically qualified to develop that resistance, at one time a tiny minority, have become the prevailing type. Likewise the genetic structure of some populations of moths has altered: dark forms have now become the prevailing forms among the sooty vegetation of an industrial countryside.[8] For all we know to the contrary, changes of this kind are the rudiments of greater evolutionary changes; and it was Darwin's theory, you remember, that they have come about because the different members of a species are endowed with different degrees of fitness: they leave more, or fewer, descendants, as the case may be, and if this happens the genetic structure of the population as a whole must clearly change.

This is all very well as far as it goes, but if we are ever to get a complete understanding of evolution we must obviously try to arrive at a complete theory of inborn variation: what forms does it take, what makes it possible, how does it happen, how is it maintained?

An analytical theory of inborn variation is one which will explain it in terms of the properties of chromosomes and nucleic acids, the substances which convey and embody genetical instructions. Let me give an example of what I mean. We can be sure that, identical twins apart, each human being alive today differs genetically from any other human being; moreover, he is probably different from any other human being who has ever lived or is likely to live in thousands of years to come. The potential variation of human beings is enormously greater than their actual variation; to put it another way, the ratio of possible men to actual men is overwhelmingly large. What mechanisms provide for the stirring about and shuffling and recombining of genetical information that makes this virtually endless diversity possible?

The most ancient and perhaps the most fundamental mechanism or stratagem that serves this function is that which is known to geneticists, in one of its forms anyway, as "crossing-over." Crossing-over is the swapping of parts between two chromosomes—a process which can occur when they have a certain general correspondence of structure; the effect of it is to combine, or recombine, genetical information in novel ways. One day biochemists and biophysicists will tell us what properties of the chromosomes make it possible for this swapping to occur. Then again: mutation, the birth of a newly variant gene, is an important process in evolution: we must ask what property or properties of the materials of heredity make mutation possible. This is the *kind* of question we must ask if we are ever to understand the pattern and progress of evolution. Let me ask another such question. If we look back upon the course of evolution we can see that within many of its lines, within many grand pedigrees of descent, there has occurred a process of becoming more complex, or, as zoologists say, more "advanced." Mammals are more "advanced" than fishes; insects are more "advanced" than worms. In the long view there has been an increase in the complexity of the genetical instructions which, so to speak, authorize an animal to be whatever it is.

If we merely confine ourselves to talking about degrees of fitness, the process seems gratuitous; what properties of the hereditary material make it understandable that it should have occurred? An explanation can only be groped after, but one kind of explanation might run something like this. The molecules of nucleic acid are of the sort that chemists describe as "polymeric": they repeat the general pattern of their structure lengthwise, and can therefore build upon themselves to increase in length. They have also the crucially important property of lending themselves to duplication, because after various chemical manoeuvres two similar molecules can be formed where there was only one before. There are many other more subtle properties of this kind; for example, the ability to break up and rejoin, to increase in length by letting in new stretches between the ends. Taken all together, these properties amount to what might be called a *repetitiousness* of nucleic acids and chromosomes, a readiness to become manifold or luxuriant or to elaborate upon genetic information—it is difficult to know which word to use. It is of the physical nature of nucleic acids that they can offer up for selection ever more complex sets of genetical instructions, can propose ever more complex solutions of the problem of remaining alive and reproducing. Every now and again one of these more complex solutions will be accepted, and so there is always a certain pre-existing inducement or authority for evolution to have what, in retrospect, we call an "upward trend."

All this is extremely lame and halting; but, as I said in my first lecture, it is a more useful way of trying to explain the phenomenon than by talking about a "vital force" of some kind which inspires organisms to advance in evolutionary history. All I am asking is: what material properties of chromosomes and nucleic acids qualify them for the functions which they do in fact discharge?

However that may be, human beings are the outcome of a process which can perfectly well be described as an advancement; and the second of the two questions I put at the beginning of this lecture was, in effect, where could we go from here?

First let me say that, even in the last fifty years, profound changes have occurred in human populations which are certainly not evolutionary changes. In some countries, for example, the average rate of growth and development has been and still is steadily going up. In the Scandinavian countries the average age of onset of first menstruation has declined between four and six months per decade for the last seventy years. In this country the height of adolescent boys has gone up by about three-quarters of an inch per decade, and their greatest height is reached by about eighteen or nineteen, instead of by twenty-five or twenty-six. These changes have been brought about by better nurture and nourishment, particularly in the first five years of life. The well-fed class may be nearing the end of this process, but the average will continue to change until the less well-fed can catch them up.[9]

Other changes have happened in human history that might conceivably be evolutionary changes. There was once a music-hall joke of uncertain import which turned on what Mr. Gladstone may or may not have said in (I hope I am right in saying) 1858. One of the things he *did* say or imply in 1858 was that colour vision may have developed in mankind since the days of Homer; for he told us that Homer's world, as Homer described it, was almost colourless; and he might have added that colour blindness does not seem to have been referred to in writing before 1684. But I understand that the poverty of colour words in Greek and other ancient languages is to be construed as lack of sensibility, not lack of sensitivity; as lack of perceptiveness, not of ability to perceive; and though full colour vision *might* have evolved within recorded history, there is no good evidence that it has done so.[10]

But evolutionary changes, as I defined them, have occurred repeatedly in human history. The rise and fall of the genetic factor responsible for sickle cell anaemia is one, and in later lectures I shall mention others. These are comparatively trivial changes: could man evolve *radically,* or be made to evolve radically, in future? I have left this question to the end because it is utterly pointless and distracting. The answer, to be delivered with every inflection of impatience, is yes indeed. The necessary conditions are satisfied: a luxuriance of inborn diversity, a system of mating that maintains it, and an unspecialized structure as the zoologist uses that word, a structure which does not in itself commit human beings to any one way of life. From the point of view of genetical evolution, human beings have retained an amateur status.

But in fussing over the nature of some great metamorphosis which might conceivably happen, but which could only happen in real life if we were to be the victims of a sustained and consistent tyranny tens of centuries long, we may forget to ask a really important question: what changes *are* happening in the genetic structure of human populations as a result of forces acting upon us now? I stand by my original decision not to attempt to predict these changes or to discuss their consequences. My question is, what kind of knowledge and understanding must we acquire about mankind, and about genetics generally, if we are to identify and predict such changes; and this is essentially what my next three lectures will be about. In my last lecture I shall give a still more cogent reason for saying that the question I put—*can* man evolve as animals may yet evolve?—is pointless, because he has in fact adopted a new kind of biological evolution (I emphasize, a biological evolution) to which a great deal of what I have said in this lecture does not apply.

# 3.

## *the limits of improvement*

Fifty years of research into human genetics has
made it clear that human beings abide by the same
laws of heredity as other animals do. There are
thousands of human pedigrees that illustrate our
conformity to the Mendelian laws.[1] I shall not bother
you with what these laws are; they are pretty well
understood, and we "obey" them in whatever sense
other organisms may be said to obey them; but if
we are to understand the genetical behaviour of a
human *population* or of any other population we
shall need to know a great deal more than that. We
shall need to know in what way and to what degree
the members of the population differ from one another, and how that diversity is maintained; to what
extent inbreeding is practised, if at all; from how
large a number and how big an area a mate may be
chosen or lighted upon; and whether "opposites at-
tract each other" or whether like mates with like.
We shall need to know how many chromosomes
there are, and what may be the importance of the
phenomenon called "linkage" in keeping the genes

on one chromosome together, or of crossing-over in letting them get apart. In short, we must try to understand the *genetic system* of human beings—not just the syntax of heredity but the whole of that which governs the flow of genetic information from one individual to another and from one generation to the next.[2] In this lecture I shall discuss the idea of a genetical system in rather general terms.

The genetic system of a species sets a limit to what it can do by way of evolving, but it is not a permanent fixture: it can itself evolve. The most important evolutionary change we ourselves have witnessed is the evolution, in hospitals, of strains of staphylococci and other bacteria which resist the action of penicillin and other antibiotic drugs. Suppose now that *antibiotin*—an antibacterial drug not yet discovered—were to come into use next year: I shall relax my self-imposed ban on soothsaying so far as to predict that, if it does so, we shall surely witness the evolution of resistant strains of bacteria.

I am saying, then, that bacteria have a genetic system which enables at least some of them to overcome misfortunes which have not yet happened, which even we ourselves cannot foresee. The idea of an organism's providing now for what may happen to it in an unknown future sounds paradoxical; but in fact makes perfectly straightforward sense. The bacteria with us today are the descendants of bacteria which, in the past, must have come through a whole succession of just such appalling hazards. Their ancestors must have come from populations which were variable enough to have contained the few odd members that could cope. The few bacteria that did cope were the ones that left descendants; but they carried with them a genetic system—a system of genetical habits, if you like—which made sure that their descendants would be as various and versatile as ever before. To say that bacteria evolved into a state of resistance on some one occasion is to tell only half the story: they must have come to possess the kind of genetic system that made it possible for that particular act of evolution to have occurred.

So much for the influence of men and their other enemies on bacteria. It is just possible that we might learn the same lesson from the effects of bacteria and *our* other enemies on *us*. In the past thousand years, we in Great Britain and in western Europe generally have had to cope with murderous irruptions of plague, leprosy, and the sweating-sickness; of great pox, small pox, diphtheria, cholera, tuberculosis, and influenza. We too, then, like bacteria, must often have been propagated through somewhat unrepresentative members of our kind—unrepresentative in the sense that, on any one occasion, those who survived an epidemic may have contained a high proportion of a genetically privileged minority. If this is a true account of the matter—and as we are still alive to wonder whether it is or not—it follows that human beings must have a genetic system which makes sure that the appropriate minorities do indeed exist.[3]

Coping with sudden attacks by infectious organisms is only one form of a problem that besets all living things: to provide not merely for *adaptedness* to the environment but for *adaptability*; to provide not only for what is happening now but for changes which, if the past is anything to go by, are all too likely to happen in the future. Moreover, it is not only a matter of the future. Although we cheerfully speak about *the* environment of an organism or a population, we know very well there is no such thing. A population of individuals lives in a range of environments, narrow or wide as the case may be; and adaptability is just as much a matter of being adapted to environments which differ from place to place as to environments which change from time to time.

In principle, we can imagine two extreme solutions of this problem of adaptability. The first would be to arrive at some one genetic constitution which endowed each individual with great versatility and great powers of accommodation and resistance, so that each one went forth into the world capable of coping with almost anything that might come its way. This constitution would have to be pretty faithfully reproduced from generation to generation; if it were not so—if when the animals bred together they produced a great variety of different offspring—then the genetic formula for being so adaptable would be lost, and the solution would lose its point.

The second solution would be to confer adaptability upon a *population* of animals without too nice a regard to the welfare and fate of its individual members, and this means adopting a genetic system with the very opposite property: one that provides for and maintains a great many inborn differences between one individual and another. If such a system were to be adopted, then, with luck, whatever happened, there would always be some members of the population who could survive and perpetuate their kind.[4]

In the past twenty years we have come to realize that most free-living organisms—perhaps all of them—adopt neither the one solution nor the other. As a biological enterprise the first has turned out to be too difficult, and the second is appallingly wasteful. What animals have adopted is a rather shifty compromise between the two.

What form does this compromise take in human beings? The answer we give to this question will colour all our thoughts about the genetic future of mankind. I feel, for example, that people who study eugenics are sometimes inclined to assume that man has adopted, or could adopt, the former of the two solutions; they have in the backs of their minds the idea of some one excellently well-adapted, all-round kind of human being who could be perpetuated according to the formula that "like begets like": in other words, by "breeding true." What I shall do now, therefore, is to discuss the kinds of inborn diversity that prevail among human beings, to see to what extent they point to the adoption of one or other of the two extreme solutions I proposed.

The inborn differences between human beings seem to be of three main kinds. First, there are the differences that divide us into a great majority and a tiny minority. Nearly all of us are lucky enough not to have haemophilia, for example, or a disease like Huntington's chorea; only about one person in a quarter of a million suffers from the bizarre abnormality that makes the urine darken when exposed to air. It is true that with the departures from normality that are said to be "fully recessive" in expression—that will not make themselves apparent unless the offending gene has been inherited from both parents—the people who carry the gene without giving evidence of it will greatly outnumber those who are actually afflicted by the disease; but, even so, it remains true to say that the great majority of us are neither the carriers of any one such harmful gene, nor the victims of its action.[5]

If this were the only kind of variation among human beings and other animals, the picture we should form in our minds of their genetic make-up would correspond to the first of the two solutions I proposed for the problem of adaptability. The commonest and fittest animal would be one that inherited a normal gene—a "good" gene, let us call it—from both its parents, and transmitted it to all its offspring; it would be *homozygous,* as the saying is, and homozygous for nearly all its genes. The same would be true of almost every other animal it could mate with, so that its offspring would have almost exactly the same genetic make-up as itself.

How then would inborn diversity arise, and how

could there be any evolution? The answer would run as follows. Unusual genes—new variants of the existing genes—arise repeatedly by the process of mutation. If the genetic make-up of an individual is as nicely adapted as we are assuming it to be, then these new genes that intrude themselves will tend to have bad effects: they will lower the fitness of their possessors; and if mutation were not, as it is known to be, a constantly recurring process, they would eventually die out. But every now and again a mutant gene would arise which conferred some advantage on its possessors; in time it would be given every opportunity to reveal its talents, because sexual reproduction, abetted by crossing-over and segregation and other genetical devices, would make sure that it was introduced into every different kind of genetic constitution the population could provide. If, in the outcome, it *did* confer an advantage, then the new gene would slowly displace the old one and become the predominant type, the normal, regular thing. While the new gene was being received into the Establishment, the population as a whole would obviously have to go through a stage in which the members who did or did not possess it were fifty-fifty; but this state of affairs would be temporary, and a portent of better things to come. According to this theory, then, inborn variety is maintained by the nagging pressure of recurrent mutation, and natural selection will almost always act in such a way as to preserve conformity, by weeding out the possessors of unusual or aberrant genes.

With some refinements I shall not go into, this was the conception that most of us had in mind as recently as twenty years ago: it is the classical conception of the elementary text books, the idea of a uniform, a predominantly homozygous population of well-adapted individuals whose offspring are almost always exactly like themselves. The idea was applied in practice to the breeding of livestock animals.

Artificial selection, it was thought, could go on smoothly until it had used up all inborn diversity in respect of the characters for which the selection was being practised; and the breeder would end up with a uniform population which met his preconceived requirements and which could be relied upon to perpetuate itself by breeding true. There were some tiresome minor snags, to be sure, and also some major difficulties. If the classical conception were wholly true, why should inbreeding, which leads to uniformity, also lead to a loss of fitness, not uncommonly to extinction? But these difficulties could be explained away, sometimes convincingly.[6] For example, if one asked why artificial selection should so often lead to a serious loss of fitness, the answer seemed reasonable enough. Artificial selection, being an arbitrary process, is almost certain to upset some hardly won and nicely adjusted natural balance between the genes. Now the great difference between artificial and natural selection is this. When judging the effectiveness of natural selection, that is selection for fitness, we are always being wise after the event; with artificial selection we are trying to be wise before the event; and what the event proves is that we are all too often ignorant.

The real weaknesses of the classical conception arise not from its being untrue but from its professing to be the whole truth. Let us try to see how far it falls short of being true of men.

There are a number of characteristics which do *not* divide human beings into a huge majority who possess them and a tiny minority who possess some alternative variant instead. The property of belonging to blood groups A or B or AB or O divides us into distinct classes of which not one is an extreme minority. The same is true of most other blood groups, and of the factors which (because there are so many of them) make it useless in the long run to patch up one human being with a skin graft taken from another, unless the two should happen to be identical twins. Variations of this kind, in which there is no question of huge majorities and tiny minorities, are described as "polymorphic," and polymorphic variation represents the second of the three kinds of ways in which I said that human beings differed. Many examples of polymorphism are known already, and a great many more are simply waiting to be discovered. Some of them are pretty ancient. Anthropoid apes have blood groups closely related to our own; and an all-star cast of exceptionally eminent geneticists was able to discern that, just like ourselves, some chimpanzees can taste and others cannot taste the compound phenylthiourea, which is extremely bitter, so I am told. So we are not dealing here with the temporary polymorphism that simply marks the ascent in the population of some newly favoured gene; nor, from what we know of the rarity of mutation, is it possible that polymorphism should be kept up by the occurrence of new mutations between one generation and the next.

At one time it was thought that polymorphism owed its commonness to its utter triviality; sometimes it was important, to be sure, but only under circumstances which could be comfortably explained away. One's blood group seemed to be a matter of complete indifference *unless* one happened to need a blood transfusion, a contingency which Nature might be excused for having overlooked. Skin grafting can indeed show that we are all innately different, but what of it? It would indeed be a splendid thing if we could repair a severe burn with a skin graft from a voluntary donor; but burns are pretty well unheard of in Nature, and nothing could be more unnatural than the grafting by which we attempt their repair.

It is now certain that polymorphism is *not* a

matter of indifference in any sense. Our subdivision into Rhesus-positive and Rhesus-negative blood groups is a qualifying condition for the occurrence of a destructive disease of the blood in new-born children—a disease which, in Great Britain, affects about one child in 150 and which caused about 400 deaths in 1957. People who are not of blood group O seem to enjoy some special protection against duodenal ulceration, particularly—and this is another polymorphism—if the chemical substances distinctive of the blood groups appear in their saliva and gastric juice as well as in their blood. People who can taste phenylthiourea seem to be slightly more liable to get one form of thyroid disease and slightly less liable to get another. These facts make little sense at present, but they do show that polymorphism is under some kind of pressure from natural selection.[7]

Polymorphism seems to arise from two main causes. The first is when, for any reason whatsoever, it is an advantage for the population to be subdivided into two or more distinct types which depend upon and therefore sustain each other. The most extreme example of this kind is the distinction between the sexes, and the mechanism that provides for *this* polymorphism has long been built into the genetic structure of higher organisms.

The other main cause of polymorphism is when, for any reason whatsoever, a so-called "heterozygote" is fitter than a homozygote. By a "heterozygote" I mean an organism that has a hybrid make-up with respect to some particular gene—that has inherited two different variants of a gene from its two parents instead of the same variant from both. I mentioned an example of this in my last lecture when I said that people whose blood contained a mixture of two different forms of haemoglobin, A and S, were more resistant to subtertian malaria than those who had only one. In this particular case a mixture is formed because its possessors are heterozygous with respect to one of the genes that govern the form of haemoglobin: instead of inheriting a gene of the same kind from both their parents, they inherited two different forms of it, one from each. And because such people are hybrids, they do not breed true. You may remember my saying that a quarter of the children of heterozygous parents have only one kind of haemoglobin, haemoglobin S. To complete the story I should add that a second quarter have the other type of haemoglobin, haemoglobin A; and the remaining half are heterozygotes like their parents.

Now consider what would follow if this state of affairs—a greater fitness of the heterozygote—were to be the universal rule. Almost everything that follows from what I called the "classical" conception would have to be withdrawn. Natural selection would no longer be a force that makes for constancy and uniformity; on the contrary, it would *oblige* populations to remain diverse, because the heterozygotes would be favoured, and heterozygotes do not breed true. Mutation, so far from being the great source of inborn diversity, would be reduced to a very minor role. We should have to abandon the idea that the fittest organism could be fixed as the overwhelmingly predominant type in the population, because, being of hybrid constitution, it would always throw off variants inferior to itself. We should be constantly frustrated in our attempts to select and establish a uniform breed of livestock animal, and artificial selection would almost always be forced to a standstill when there was still plenty of inborn diversity in the population—but a diversity which, unfortunately, could not be used.[8]

The state of affairs I have just described is no more the whole truth than that which is envisaged by the "classical" conception, but it is a greater part of the truth than we suspected twenty years ago.

The origin of the superior fitness of the heterozygous constitution, when it is superior, is one of the mysteries of modern genetics. We can sometimes discern reasons why, in any one particular case, the heterozygote should be superior; but I can think of only one *general* reason why it should so often have tended to become so, and it is this: a free-living species whose members have to cope with environments which change from time to time and differ from place to place will tend to acquire a genetic system which forcibly maintains a certain pattern of genetic inequality or inborn variety. This is one possible solution of the problem of providing for adaptability—a solution to which most free-living organisms are to some extent committed. This argument may be quite mistaken: there may be no *general* reason why heterozygotes should often be the fittest organisms, or, if there is a general reason, it may not be the one I have outlined. But whether there is one reason or a multitude of particular reasons, there seems no doubt that some large part of human fitness is vested in a mechanism which provides for a high degree of genetic inequality and inborn diversity, which makes sure that there are plenty of different kinds of human beings; and this fact sets a limit to any purely theoretical fancies we may care to indulge in about the perfectibility of men.

I have left to the end the third of the three ways in which human beings may differ from one another, because I shall discuss it at greater length in my next two lectures. Most characteristics do *not* divide us into sharply distinct classes of the sort I have been discussing so far. Our heights, or wits, or, over the normal range of variation, our blood-pressures form a smoothly graded series; tallness or shortness, brightness or dullness, are simply stretches of a continuous range. The inheritance of differences of this kind behaves as if it were due to the co-operation and interaction of a very large number of genes; and the same goes for some characteristics that do necessarily divide us into distinct classes, like the number of children one can have or the number of hairs on one's head. Many differences that have a direct bearing on fitness are inherited in this fashion —differences of fecundity itself, for example, or growth-rate, or length of life.

Unhappily, the study of this form of inheritance, "metrical" inheritance, is exceptionally difficult, both in theory and practice; but I think that research has gone far enough to reveal here, too, the workings of a compromise between the two extreme solutions of the problem of providing for adaptability.

I said earlier, you may remember, that if the classical conception represented the whole truth, a programme of artificial selection could proceed quite smoothly until all inborn diversity had been used up—a limit which would not be reached until the genes affecting the characters under selection had been fixed in their true-breeding, that is, their homozygous, form. If, on the other hand, animals of hybrid constitution were always the fittest, then the attempt to fix some desired kind of animal would be an uphill struggle, constantly opposed and usually frustrated by the fact that the fittest animals did not breed true. What then are the results of experiments on the selection of metrical characters? In general, steady progress is made to begin with, and the results begin to take shape as if the classical conception were true; but after a number of generations of selection, it usually becomes clear that something is going seriously wrong: the stock begins to deteriorate in fitness and may even die out. A limit to improvement is reached when there is still plenty of inborn variation, but variation of a kind that is not accessible or not amenable to selection.

There is known to be more than one reason why this limit should be arrived at, but one important reason does indeed seem to be superior fitness conferred by the heterozygous make-up. Attempts at selection are, in fact, torn between conflicting interests: the characters we are hoping to establish and fix in the population—height or weight, perhaps, or, in the fruit-flies that are so often used for these experiments, bristliness—may well find their most extreme expression in the true-breeding homozygous form; but that is not going to be much consolation if these homozygous forms are inferior in fitness, and are therefore at a constant disadvantage compared with the forms that do not breed true. Artificial selection and natural selection pull opposite ways.[9]

The experiments which reveal the compromise I have been discussing were done on animals, but there is no reason at all to suppose that their results do not apply to men. Human beings, too, are to some extent committed to a genetic system which attaches a certain weight, perhaps great weight, to there being many different kinds of men. This state of affairs is part of a very ancient genetic heritage: it came about, perhaps, because no species of free-living animal which survives to give evidence on the matter can ever have achieved adaptedness by the total sacrifice of adaptability; and the maintenance of a high degree of inborn variety is one way, wasteful but biologically easy, by which adaptability can be achieved.[10]

Fortunately, there is now a new solution of the problem of providing for adaptability, and it goes some way towards making up for these inborn inequalities and imperfections of men which the older solution necessarily entails. This newer solution is to *improve the environment,* whether by a comparatively simple method like eradicating malaria or tuberculosis, or by the grander enterprise of attempting to cure all human ills and deficiencies. There is sound biological sense in this solution: Nature, hitherto, has been somewhat inept, and has reconciled herself to compromises; she can do better now. The extremely difficult and ingenious trick which has made it possible for human beings to adopt this newer solution I shall try to explain in my final lecture. For the present, I should like you to notice that it is the *humane* solution too ("humaneness," according to the dictionary, means "characterized by such behaviour or disposition towards others as befits a man"). It will be important to contrast the picture I shall finally arrive at with that older social biology which said "Three cheers for Natural Selection," "the devil take the hindmost" —and much else about Nature's teeth and claws. As some biologists did at one time connive at the acceptance of this manifesto, I should perhaps mention that it is based upon a technical misunderstanding of Nature, of man's place in Nature, and of the nature of man.

# 4.

## the genetic system of man

Sir Francis Galton, the founder of Eugenics, a humane and highly gifted man, tried to think of some reason why so many noble lineages should have died out for want of heirs. To be exact, he asked himself why twelve out of thirty-one peerages conferred upon English judges from the days of Queen Elizabeth had become extinct, and why six others had come perilously near extinction. The solution he hit upon was this. The peers had married heiresses. An heiress worth marrying for the size of her legacy must have come from a very small family: if she had had a brother or many sisters, her legacy could hardly have been so great. In the days when families were so much larger, a small family was usually a sign that the parents were unable to have more children—not a sign that they chose to have no more. Differences in the ability to have children are strongly inherited: somewhat infertile parents tend to have somewhat infertile children. And so the noble lines died out through an inheritance of infertility.[1]

Let us set aside improving thoughts about the evils of avarice and of a desire for self-aggrandisement, and draw only this particular moral: that where monogamy prevails, the fertility of a marriage is limited by the less fertile partner: one partner sterile sterilizes both. This is one example of how social habits or conventions may affect the genetic welfare of mankind. Monogamous marriage is part of the genetic system of most human beings. In my previous lecture I described the genetic system of a species as the whole of that which affects the flow of genetic information from one individual to another and from one generation to the next, and I discussed the idea of a genetic system in very general terms. The time has now come to point more directly at some of the factors which may influence the genetic make-up of human populations.

It is extremely difficult to think of any social habit or act of legislation that has *no* genetic consequences. Penal, fiscal, social, moral, medical, political, or educational laws, schemes, treatments, habits or observances will all make *some* mark on our genetic structure.[2] Advances in the application of medicine have changed the entire pattern of the forces of mortality. Taxation which falls unequally upon people with different innate endowments will affect the number of children they have, and therefore the genetic make-up of future generations. Differences of educability are to some extent inherited. Most educated parents want their children to enjoy their own advantages—a costly ambition, sometimes; and to achieve it they sometimes have fewer children than they might have wished. Migration will intermingle people with different genetic constitutions. It may be a matter of movement from village to village in an agricultural community, or it can take place on a colossal scale: between 1820 and 1950 some 40,000,000 foreigners entered the United States. Economic pressures can promote migration and political action can stop it; both, then, may have genetic effects.[3]

But intermixture does not follow inevitably from migration. By marrying mainly among themselves, people who observe the Jewish religion retain a certain racial distinctness: their blood groups are characteristically those of eastern Mediterranean peoples; their finger-prints belong to a distinctive family of patterns; they are almost exempt from some hereditary diseases and almost the only victims of others. Jewish people owe their integrity to a special form of *assortative mating,* the mating of like with like.[4] The tendency of people of the same educational standing to marry each other has to be kept firmly in mind when trying to weigh up the heritability of intelligence; and the same applies to marriages between people of the same temperament or physique. Assortative mating between people of the same economic or social standing will tend to produce a genetical stratification of the community, but migration from class to class will tend to break that differentiation down.

*Inbreeding* could be classified as a form of assortative mating. Inbreeding makes for genetic uniformity, and its effect upon species like ours, genetically adapted to outbreeding, is invariably bad. For example, very rare hereditary disorders turn up much more frequently among the children of marriages between first cousins than among the population as a whole.[5] As a general rule the Roman Catholic Church does not allow marriages between first cousins—another example of how religious observances may have genetic consequences.

There are other less obvious but perhaps more important ways in which our social structure can affect our genetic make-up. A man may not always choose an occupation that will turn his inborn abilities to their best advantage, but he will often choose an occupation in which his disadvantages show up least. In children's comic papers, the scholarly youth can be identified not only by his earnest expression but by his spectacles and his spots. The inference we are presumably expected to draw is that long poring over books has deranged his vision and brought on an impurity of the blood; but I detect also the faint implication that his scholarly habits were brought on by his poor eyesight or his sickly constitution: it was because the lad could not take to football that he took to books. From the neolithic revolution onwards—perhaps for the past 10,000 years—the tendency of men to occupy the niches in a complex society for which their constitution fitted them, or failed to unfit them, must have played a very important part in the enrichment of mankind.[6]

Obviously, then, a multitude of social forces can affect the genetic make-up of human populations. But the great problem is: what is the nature and magnitude of their effects? Sometimes, in a modest way, we can predict them. Assortative mating will keep negroes and whites genetically apart in America or South Africa—though we hardly need a geneticist to tell us that. The consequences of inbreeding and of marriages between first cousins can be foretold in general terms. Our knowledge of simple mendelian heredity in human beings makes it possible to forecast the kind of children that will issue from certain marriages, and our powers of prediction would be greatly strengthened if it were always possible to identify the potential parents of victims of so-called "recessive diseases."[7] Again, it is a fact that radiations increase the rate of mutation, and that nearly all mutant genes which are obtrusive in their action are harmful. So far as we understand its effects, therefore, radiation is indeed a genetic insult to mankind. We know enough, I think, to be able to say that hybridization between people of different races need not be expected to lead to an improvement, because both races will probably have adopted the well-balanced genetic constitution that matches their own environments; on the other hand, it might prove favourable in the long run because hybridization enriches diversity and might therefore produce a more versatile genetic structure than before. But we cannot be sure.

There is indeed an immense amount that we cannot be sure about. Yet, in spite of that, you will have heard it said that the fall of nations can be traced to genetic causes—for example, to the persistent infertility of a ruling class; you have been alarmed by insistent declarations that we are declining rapidly in intelligence; you have been stirred by the pronouncement that man can now control his own evolution; you have admired the easy assurance with which some people put a genetic interpretation upon differences of temperament and character—of the qualities that make for leadership or bravery or co-operativeness, or for economic success; and you have been taken aback by the confidence with which some experts will assert what other experts will just as confidently deny. The idea that a man's genetic constitution is not merely important but all-important, and that genetic knowledge is so far advanced that we can make nice judgments about our past or future genetic health, together add up to the doctrine or state of mind which, to be in the fashion of these things, should be called *geneticism*. Geneticism is the application to human affairs (or indeed to livestock breeding or natural selection or evolution) of a genetic knowledge or understanding which is assumed to be very much greater than it really is. It may surprise you to know that there is still no comprehensive theory of the improvement of livestock animals by selection. Geneticists have made great progress with their attempts to substitute sound genetic principles for an empiricism of do's and don'ts; but until those principles have been established, it might be as well to forbear from grandiose prophetic or retrospective utterances about the genetic welfare of mankind.

The same goes for our understanding of evolution. Twenty years ago it all seemed easy: with mutation as a source of diversity, with selection to pick and choose, and with a mainly homozygous make-up to be aimed at, all we were left to wonder about was why on earth evolution should be so slow. But we know now that natural populations are obstinately diverse in their genetic make-up, and that the devices which make them so are bound to make them rather resistant to evolutionary change. Our former complacency can be traced, I suppose, to an understandable fault of temperament: scientists tend not to ask themselves questions until they can see the rudiments of an answer in their minds. Embarrassing questions tend to remain unasked or, if asked, to be answered rudely. That is why I thought it important, in a previous lecture, to put an innocent question about the causes of evolutionary advancement. And here is another: why does so much of evolution lend itself to a belief in the inheritance of acquired characters? As I shall explain in my final lecture, belief in Lamarckism—in the idea that the environment can somehow issue genetic instructions to living organisms—is founded upon a misconception far wider than merely concerns genetics; but the question I put—how comes it that a Lamarckian style of inheritance should be so astutely imitated?—must still be asked, though I shall not have time at present to explain how an answer has been taking shape.[8]

In the years since the war, the study of selection and evolution has undergone an important change of emphasis, one which is highly relevant to our attempt to interpret the action of genetic forces on mankind. I should like now to give you a general idea of what has been going on.

In my last lecture I classified the inborn differences between human beings. First, you may remember, there are characteristics that divide us into sharply distinct categories: we either have or have not the particular defect which makes itself apparent as haemophilia or as phenylketonuria; our blood group is *either* A *or* AB *or* B *or* O. If all such differences were to be discovered— a great many have been— then each human being could be labelled and identified by his possessing a certain particular *combination* of alternative genes. Mr. X, we should say, is of blood group A (as opposed to B) and of M (as opposed to N); he is Rhesus positive (as opposed to Rhesus negative)—and so on for all his characteristics, not merely the properties of his blood. This system of labelling would confirm us in a straightforwardly atomistic conception of evolution—in the belief that the units of inheritance and evolution were always certain particular things called "genes." [9]

But then I mentioned another kind of difference —that which divides us not into sharply distinct classes but by gradations or degrees. So with height or shape or intelligence; with fertility and growth rate and length of life; and presumably with character and temperament as well. I said that these smoothly graded differences behaved as if they were under the combined control of a very large number of particular genes. Inheritance of this kind is accordingly described as "polygenic." Inheritance of the other kind can be called "segregative" because it separates us into clear and well-defined groups.

Segregative differences were the first to be analysed successfully and they are the first we learn about when we study genetics. A number of early attempts to investigate what we now call polygenic inheritance came to grief because the principle of mendelian heredity had not yet come to light: the principle that the inborn differences between organisms do *not* tend to decay and disappear as a result of a *blending* of characteristics. On the contrary, mendelian heredity works in such a way that the proportion of individuals having one genetic make-up or another can be assumed to remain constant from generation to generation unless something special happens to prevent its being so. This was a discovery of Newtonian stature, and it can be put, if we like, in a Newtonian style: the genetic structure of a randomly interbreeding population remains constant from generation to generation except in so far as some impressed force (like natural selection) is brought to bear upon it. Just as for Newton it was not motion but *change* of motion that called for a special explanation, so it is a change of genetic structure that demands to be explained. So far as we know, mendelian inheritance, in this general sense of a conservation of inborn diversity, is a principle that applies to the whole of genetic inheritance; but it must on no account be confused with what is sometimes called "mendelizing heredity" or "simple mendelian inheritance"—the three-to-one ratios you may have heard of, or the comparatively simple rules that are relied upon when a matter of disputed parentage is brought to law. This simple mendelian inheritance is something of a special case.

The historical order in which genetic discoveries were made, and the order in which we were taught them, incline us to forget an important truth: that polygenic inheritance is the general rule and that segregative inheritance is always unusual and sometimes freakish. What is so unusual about segregative inheritance is this: that the genes to which we attribute it have pretty well the same effects no matter what the rest of a man's genetic constitution may be. With the very rarest exceptions, the gene that turns Mr. X into someone of blood group A will also turn Mr. Y into someone of blood group A, no matter how different Mr. X and Mr. Y may be in other respects. This state of affairs, as I say, is unusual; and because it has this unusual character, the inheritance of differences between our blood groups can be seen to obey the simple mendelian rules. And what I meant by the word "freakish" was this. If some complex chain of chemical processes is necessary for the normal working of the body, then any mutation which breaks one link in that chain will cause a pretty obvious and far-reaching abnormality. A mutant gene of this kind will almost always make itself apparent, no matter what the rest of the constitution may be; and because its effect is both obtrusive and uncompromising, its inheritance will be seen to obey simple mendelian rules. This is why so much of the human heredity that is studiable reads like a doctor's case-book; but the forms of heredity that can be seen to obey fairly simple rules are not a representative sample of heredity as a whole.

The trouble is that the whole way in which we think about genetics has grown up round these somewhat unusual cases; and, as a result of this, we are under a constant psychological pressure to think of polygenic inheritance as if it were just a highly complicated form of simple segregative inheritance—as if it were elementary mendelism scored for a full symphony orchestra. But polygenic inheritance must be studied in its own right. Without doubt it has many regularities, analogous to those we see in ordinary segregative inheritance; but most of them have yet to be discovered. The study of polygenic inheritance and of the effects of selection upon graded, measurable characters is still in its beginnings. Its analysis is time-consuming and very difficult. The people who study it are confronted by strange and at present inexplicable phenomena. They are the last people in the world to make cock-sure predictions about the consequences of selection—least of all about selection as it affects the welfare and destiny of man. It is not true that we now know how to control our own evolution—if by "control" is meant directing it towards a predetermined goal. We are *not* entitled by our present knowledge to put a genetical construction upon the rise and fall of nations. We do *not* understand the inheritance of differences of temperament or character; all we do know about the matter is what we have learnt from the evolution of tameness or docility in domesticated animals: that some such characters are under some kind of genetical control.[10]

This does not mean that we have to preserve a selfrighteous silence until further bulletins are issued from genetical back rooms. We can already use to very good purpose our knowledge of human medical genetics, which is mainly a genetics of segregative differences, for the reasons I have just explained. We can call attention to what seem to be dangers according to present ways of thinking—for example, to the decline of human intelligence which I shall discuss later. We can expose fallacies when they are cruel (like the belief that imbecility is the symptom of a general decay of the genetic constitution) or when they are merely silly, like the belief that some special virtue travels down the male (as opposed to the female) line of descent.[11] And then we can make cautious statements about the effects, so far as we understand them, of certain genetical practices or habits. One of the questions I put in my first lecture was this: is the practice of bith control and family limitation so unnatural that it is bound to have evil consequences? This is a question of great practical importance, so let me spend the rest of this lecture discussing what the consequences of birth control might be.

Two distinct things are involved in a deliberate limitation of the size of families, and they must be kept apart. The first is a restriction of the total number of children born to a married couple; the second is a tendency which need not go with it, though it usually does—a tendency to complete a family earlier in life than would otherwise have been the case.[12] I shall discuss the second first.

The most general effect of an earlier completion of families will be to shorten the average gap between successive generations: one generation will follow another more quickly, so that whatever genetical changes are happening will happen faster in terms of calendar years. More particularly, we can look forward to a sharp decline in the numbers of newborn children afflicted by mongolian idiocy or by any other disease that increases in frequency with their mother's age. We can expect the sex ratio at birth to shift still further in favour of males, with the consequence that, for the first time perhaps, men will outnumber women in their marriageable years. We can expect, too, a decline in the frequency of ordinary (that is non-identical) twinning.[13]

A less obvious and much less important effect will be to relax the pressure of natural selection against inherited abnormalities which can defer their outward appearance until about the middle of life: I have in mind abnormalities like Huntington's chorea, manic depressive psychoses, and certain forms of cancer. On the whole, these diseases do not disqualify their victims from parenthood until *after* most of their children have been born—from which it follows that the genes responsible for them will have been passed on before natural selection has much opportunity to intercede. An earlier completion of families will reduce the force of selection still further—a matter of minor importance, perhaps, but not altogether negligible.[14]

So much seems fairly clear: the rest is a matter of guesswork. An earlier completion of families implies that a human pedigree will hereafter run through a succession of rather younger mothers—mothers much younger, on the average, than they would have been a hundred years ago. This may just conceivably be a good thing, for the following reason. It is now widely agreed that human egg-cells do not increase in number after birth: women make do with the entirely adequate number they have to begin with, and the egg-cells are used up progressively in course of life. This means that egg-cells are obliged to wait for years in the ovary before they are shed into the Fallopian tube, where they may or may not be fertilized. Too long a wait, repeated generation after generation, might just possibly be harmful. It would be very interesting to study the recorded pedigrees of noble families and trace the fate of the lineages that went through last daughters of last daughters of last daughters. I must tell you that when an experiment which reproduces this state of affairs is carried out on animals called *rotifers,* the lines of descent that pass repeatedly through older mothers invariably die out. But then rotifers are very lowly and highly aberrant pond animalcules; it would be most unsound to draw far-reaching conclusions from a comparison between rotifers and human beings of noble birth.[15]

A restriction of the total number of children has several genetic consequences, one of which is to make the work of human geneticists even more difficult than it already is. It will certainly reduce the frequency of all diseases of children—above all haemolytic disease of newborn children—which tend to take a more severe form or to occur more often in the later children of a family. But it has one effect which is genetically unfavourable, though on a rather microscopic scale. When married couples plan to have fewer children than they could have had, they can, and sometimes do, make up for the loss of one child by having another. If a child has been lost through the manifestation in it of some highly damaging recessive gene—of a gene that must be inherited from *both* parents if it is to make its presence felt—then there is a two-thirds chance that the normal child which might replace it will be a carrier, though not a victim, of that harmful gene. To some very slight degree, therefore, the effect of natural selection will be circumvented, for the harmful gene will circulate just a little more freely in the population than would otherwise have been the case.[16]

But what people really fear when they talk about the biological evils of birth control is this. In many countries, families are deliberately restricted to two or three or four. The pressure of natural selection against low degrees of fertility will therefore be, to some extent, relaxed. I mean that if families now average only two or three children, there will no longer be the same sharp discrimination between married couples who *could* only have had two or three children and those who, had they wished it, could have had ten or twelve. Some discrimination there surely will be; but it is theoretically possible that in a matter of tens or hundreds of generations the proportion of innately very fertile men and women may go down.

If this were to happen, I think it would be looked back upon as an example—yet another example— of the way in which the level of fertility comes to be adapted to the prevailing circumstances. It is a fallacy to assume, as I fear some biologists still do assume, that the fertility of a species is a kind of primeval fixture—as if animals and plants were driven by some demon of fertility to have vastly more offspring than are needed. One can hear it said that the explanation of natural selection itself is that living things produce an allegedly "prodigious" number of offspring, of which only a chosen few are spared. But to say this is to forget that the level of fertility adopted by any species is just as much the *consequence* of natural selection as its cause. There is in fact no good reason to fear that an innate decline of human fertility must be a stage on the road to extinction or that we shall face a struggle to keep mankind alive.

Of course, one can imagine circumstances in which a low level of fertility might be very disadvantageous. Some frightful disaster might oblige a handful of human beings to populate the entire world anew. But why worry about the imaginary dangers of a low level of fertility in the distant future when confronted by the real dangers of a high level of fertility as it affects so many countries of the world today? These are real and present worries; yet one of them at least we can spare ourselves: on present evidence, there is no reason to believe that the world-wide adoption of the practice of birth control would have biologically malign effects. On the contrary, there is every reason to believe that failure to adopt some measure of family limitation will lead, in the long run, to misery, privation, and economic distress.

# 5.

## *intelligence and fertility*

A cultured lady declares that now at last she understands why so many of El Greco's figures seem to us to be unnaturally tall and thin. It is because El Greco had a certain defect of vision which made him *see* people with that particular distortion; and as he saw them, so he drew them. But a child then pipes up with the following objection: "Surely if his eyes made everything look too tall and thin, wouldn't he see his own pictures in a different way from us too, and wouldn't they look just as strange to him as they do to us? If *all* he was doing was painting people in the funny way he saw them, then surely his paintings would *have* to look all right to us if they were going to look all right to him."

What an irritating child! But—what an intelligent one! There is a grasp here, an ability to reason, to follow an argument and detect its faults. These qualities, and others like them, add up to "intelligence"; and in this lecture I propose to discuss the possibility that in some countries, Great Britain among them, the average level of human intelligence is going down.

If we classify children of any chosen age by the scores they get in intelligence tests, and then make a diagram showing what number or proportion were awarded each possible score, we shall find that the diagram is smooth and pretty well symmetrical. The average score divides the children equally, and the most numerous single group is the one whose members have this average and middling score. Moreover, the number of children who exceed the average by a certain quantity is about equal to the number who fall short of the average by that quantity; and as we get further and further from the average in either direction, so the number of children to be counted gets less and less.

What I have said about the distribution of scores in intelligence tests applies to other characteristics of human beings—to the heights of adult men or women, for example. Within the whole range of heights and wits there are people who are exceptional in the sense of being in a minority—uncommonly good at intelligence tests, or uncommonly small; but to call them "abnormal" is a bit misleading, because it suggests that they are separated from the rest of us by sharp divisions or bold steps. It is true that some people do lie right outside the normal range of variation—are abnormally small or abnormally dull for reasons that call for special explanations. So it is with idiots and imbeciles: those who fall short of the average to the degree of utter incapability do seem to form a class apart.[1]

But it is no longer these unlucky people that biologists have in mind when they discuss the possibility that intelligence may be declining. Many years ago, to be sure, the rumour got around that mankind would lose its wits because idiots and imbeciles are riotously fertile.[2] In fact they are nothing of the kind. Many are sterile; and in any event confinement to home or homes makes it impossible for most of them to have children—a good example of what I discussed in my last lecture, the way in which legislation (in this case the laws of certification) can have genetic effects. No: the problem arises over the greater fertility of those who are somewhat below the average of intelligence; and the fear is that their progeny are tending to crowd the rest of the population out. This might happen for one or both of two reasons: because, generation by generation, they tend to have larger families than the more intelligent; or because, generation by generation, they tend to have them earlier in life. For if the more intelligent parents start having children later and space them more widely apart, then, even if they end up with the same size of family in the long run, they are bound to be left behind.

All rational discussion of the possibility that intelligence may be declining starts from our knowledge of a certain association between the average performance of children in intelligence tests and the size of the families they belong to: in some countries, Great Britain among them, children who belong to small families are known to do better in intelligence tests than the children of larger families. The relationship between the average score of children and the number of their brothers and sisters is pretty consistent over the whole range of family sizes: taken by and large, children with $x$ brothers and sisters do better than children with $x$ + 1. A great mass of evidence points to a clear *negative correlation* between the size of a family and the average performance of its members.[3]

Before asking how this negative correlation is to be explained, and what its genetic implications may be, we must take some view about what is to be inferred from a score in an intelligence test. Some people speak with angry contempt of "*so-called* intelligence tests"; having satisfied themselves of the absurdity of claims which psychologists no longer make for them (and which the better psychologists never did make), they dismiss the entire subject from their minds. Others profess to attach no meaning to the word "intelligence"—but try calling them *un*intelligent and see how they react. At the risk of being peremptory, because time is short, I shall take the view that intelligence tests measure intellectual aptitudes which are important, though very far from all-important; and that these aptitudes make up a significant fraction of what we all of us call "intelligence" in everyday life. Only one disclaimer is important: intelligence tests can be valuable when they are applied to children still at school and to feeble-minded adults; their application to adults in general is very much more restricted in scope.

There are quite a number of possible explanations of the negative correlation between intelligence and family size. One possibility is that, for some reason, a child's intelligence declines with his position in the family; the first child being the most intelligent; the last, the least. The intelligence of each child might depend upon the age of his mother when she bore him, for a mother must be older when she bears (say) her fourth child than when she bears her third. This idea goes against all common understanding, but for purely technical reasons it is rather difficult to test. If we set aside certain forms of imbecility which are obviously exceptional, the most accurate tests show that matters to do with rank of birth do *not* explain the relationship between intelligence and family size.[4]

A second possibility is that size of family can itself affect a child's proficiency in those intelligence tests which rely heavily upon some outward or inward skill in the use of words. For one thing, a child in a large family will listen and contribute much more to the unscholarly prattle of its brothers and sisters than will a child in a family of two or three. There is good evidence that inexperience in the use of words does play some part in the negative correlation between scores in intelligence tests and family size. It seems entirely reasonable that it should. Words are not merely the vehicles in which thought is delivered: they are part of thinking; and lack of experience in the use of words, even unspoken words, may well put a child at a disadvantage in a test.[5]

There is a less direct way in which the size of the family he belongs to might be related to a child's performance. On the whole children of large families are not quite so tall, at any given age of childhood, as the children of smaller families—perhaps because, on the average, they have been a little less well nourished. They grow more slowly, therefore, though they might make up for that disadvantage by continuing their growth a little longer, ending up no smaller than the better fed. But if, at any chronological age, the children of large families are a little backward physically, might they not be backward in mental growth as well? And may they not eventually catch up with the others, given a little time? Mental and physical growth are not exactly in gear, so backwardness in size can by no means be construed as backwardness of mind; but so far as our meagre evidence goes, there is some small but definite connexion between the intelligence of children and their size at any given age of childhood; and, with some reservations, this might account for a certain small part of the negative correlation between intelligence and family size.[6]

Another possibility is that a lowly score in an intelligence test is part of a child's inheritance from its parents, though not an inheritance in the technical or genetic sense. Unintelligent parents, we might reason, have large families because they have neither the skill nor the will to have smaller families; and, being unintelligent, their conversation and precepts will tend to have a rudely pragmatical character, and their houses to be bare of books. The nature of the home he comes from is known to affect a child's performance in verbal tests of intelligence; but there is no suggestion here that a child of unintelligent parents would be at any disadvantage if he were to be brought up in a more educated home.

Yet another possibility is that the children of less intelligent parents do *not* start on the same footing as the children of the more intelligent; that their lack of intelligence is something which good upbringing can palliate but cannot completely cure; that differences of intelligence are inherited in the technical or genetic sense.

At this point I shall ask you to assume (what I think no one denies) that differences of intelligence *are* to some degree inborn. There are certain obstinate and persistent correlations of intelligence between parents and their children and between the children of a family among themselves—correlations that do not disappear when as much allowance as possible is made for differences of upbringing, environment, and family size. The study of these correlations in the population generally, and, in particular, of the values they take in foster-children and in identical twins who have been reared apart, suggests that not less than half of the observed variation of intelligence is an inborn variation. For many environments, it may be a good deal more than half. It does not do to be more particular, because the concept of an inborn variation in characters greatly affected by the environment is very complex, and the people who know most about it are the least inclined to express it in a numerically exact form.[7]

Let us agree, then, that differences of intelligence

are strongly inherited. We must now ask, why do less intelligent parents run to larger families? Teachers, demographers and social workers incline to believe that the answer is mainly this. Less intelligent parents have larger families because they are less well informed about birth control or less skilful in its practice; because they are less well able to see the material disadvantages of having more children than can be well provided for, or the more than material advantages of having the children one really wants. I do not like to put it this way because it seems to import a moral judgment which, valid or not, has no bearing on the argument. Someone might insist that it was *right* for all parents to have all the children they were capable of having, and that the unintelligent live up to that precept because, being more innocent than learned but worldly people, they have a clearer perception of what is right or wrong. All this is beside the point. The point is that they have more children, and are unintelligent, whether that does them credit or not; and if they do have more children, there is a certain presumption that innate intelligence in the population at large will decline. It should not decline at anything like the speed suggested by the boldly negative correlation between intelligence and size of family, because, as we have agreed, some part of that correlation can be traced to causes in which inborn differences of intelligence need play no part.

I say there is a *presumption* that the average level of intelligence will decline. It is not a certainty. In the first place, one highly important piece of information is missing. What about the intelligence of married couples who have no children, or of people who never marry at all? Those who are oppressed by the possibility of a decline of intelligence point, with some reason, at the many highly learned people who are childless; and they remind us that when a population is classified by the occupations of its members, something is to be learned from the fact that manual labourers are much more fertile than those who live mainly on their wits. But those who think that the dangers of a decline are greatly exaggerated point out that idiots and imbeciles, and some of the feeble minded, are very infertile too. Our uncertainty about the intelligence of those who have no children is awkward because it means that we cannot give a very confident answer to a very important question: to what extent are the parents of each successive generation a representative sample of the population of which they form a part?

A second reason for saying that the decline of intelligence is no more than a presumption is that there can obviously be no certainty in the matter until we know exactly how differences of intelligence are inherited. The argument for a decline is based on the belief that differences of intelligence are under the control of a multitude of genes, no one of which can be recognized individually; and it is assumed that the contributions of these genes to intelligence are *additive* in a certain technical sense. Are these assumptions justifiable? There is no reason at all to doubt that inborn differences of intelligence over the normal range of variation are under the control of a very large number of genes; but the idea that their contributions are additive requires a little consideration.

The word "additive" refers to a particular pattern of co-operation of interaction between genes. An additive pattern of interaction implies (amongst other things) that there will be no such thing as hybrid vigour in respect of intelligence; it implies that a person who is mainly heterozygous or hybrid in his make-up with respect to the many genes that control intelligence will lie somewhere between the extremes of brightness or dullness that correspond to those genes in their similar or homozygous forms.[8] If, on the contrary, the genes that controlled differences of intelligence were all to exert their greatest effect in the hybrid or heterozygous state, then there would be no correlation between the intelligences of parents and their children: the children of parents who both had the high intelligence conferred by a hybrid make-up would as often as not be of low intelligence, and parents of low intelligence would as often as not give birth to children much more intelligent than themselves. But in actual fact the correlation of intelligence between parents and children is just as great as the correlation between the children of a family among themselves, so there is no good reason to doubt that the genes interact in the manner which I have described as additive. Nor, as I say, is there any reason whatsoever to doubt that a great many genes are at work. Both assumptions I have made are therefore justifiable, and there is a fair case for the belief that intelligence is declining. There is an equally good case for the belief that the decline could not go on indefinitely, but this, for the moment, I shall defer.

Is there any *direct* evidence that intelligence is declining? In 1932, a grand survey was made of the scores in intelligence tests of 90,000 Scottish schoolchildren whose eleventh birthdays fell within that year. Fifteen years later, in 1947, a very similar test was carried out on some 70,000 children of the same ages. No decline was apparent: the boys' scores had improved slightly; the performance of girls had risen even more. Taken together, the children of 1947 were two or three months ahead of the children of 1932 in terms of mental age.[9]

At first sight these results were immensely reassuring. A decline of intelligence on the scale we now fear might not have been shown up by tests only fifteen years apart; but an increase was more than most people had dared to hope for. But could anything have happened to conceal a genuinely innate decline? Unhappily it could. The children of

1947 were, on the average, an inch and a half taller than their predecessors of 1932. They were ahead in physical as well as in mental age; [10] but this does not imply that they were bound to end up taller and brighter when they reached adult stature of body and mind. Again, the pattern of family sizes might have altered in those fifteen years. If it did, the alteration would surely have taken the form of a decline in the proportion of the largest families, and this alone would account for a certain rise of average score. There is much else besides. The children of 1932 were taught by methods that may not have prepared them so well for intelligence tests; they grew up when a wireless set had not yet become a voluble piece of ordinary household furniture, and they lacked, then, whatever experience in "verbalization" (if you will pardon the expression) comes from a constant familiarity with the spoken word.

But still: I gave you theoretical reasons for thinking that there might be a slow decline of intelligence, and direct evidence which, taken at its face value, shows that no such decline occurred. Can the theory itself be incomplete or wrong?

Some geneticists believe that it is incomplete, and I should like to explain their reasons. I asked a moment ago why the less intelligent should run to larger families, and gave the answer that has seemed reasonable to most of us: they have larger families for reasons connected with their lack of intelligence. But some geneticists look to another explanation: that people of mediocre or rather lowly intelligence are intrinsically more fertile, innately more capable of having children, than people of very high or very low intelligence.

To accept this interpretation is by no means to deny that inborn differences of intelligence are controlled by a multitude of genes, or that inborn variation of intelligence is mainly additive in character.

A new point is being made: that people of mainly heterozygous make-up are innately more fertile— are innately *fitter,* as biologists use that word. When people of mediocre intelligence marry and have children, then, in the simplest possible case, some half of their children will grow up to be like themselves; the other half will consist of relatively infertile people of very high and of very low intelligence in about equal numbers. The children of each successive generation will therefore be recruited mainly from parents of mediocre intelligence, but they will always include among them the very bright and the very dull. It is possible, as a theoretical exercise, to construct a balance sheet of intelligence in which gains and losses cancel each other out: a reservoir of parents of mediocre or even lowly intelligence maintains a natural and stable equilibrium in the population, for, among their children, the all but complete sterility of low-grade mental defectives will cancel with the lesser fertility of the very bright.[11]

There is one respect, I think, in which this argument carries a lot of weight. It sets a natural limit to any likely rise or fall of intelligence. If a tyrant were to carry out an experiment on human selection, in an attempt to raise the intelligence of all of us to its present maximum, or to degrade it to somewhere near the minimum that now prevails, then I feel sure that his attempts would be self-defeating: the population would dwindle in numbers and, in the extreme case, might die out. In the long run, the superior fitness of heterozygotes would frustrate his dastardly schemes.[12] This is a cheering hypothesis, but it does not imply, I fear, that our population is already in a state of equilibrium; that the average level of intelligence may not fall a good deal further yet. It does not imply that we have already used up all the resources of additive genetic variation that can be called upon before natural selection intervenes. Nothing could be more unrealistic than to suppose that our population is already in a state of natural and stable equilibrium, with a nice balance between gain of intelligence and loss. We cannot disregard the purely arbitrary element in whatever it is that decides the size of a family—disregard the massive evidence of the Royal Commission on Population on the spread of the practice of birth control.[13] Nor can we neglect the fact that habits of fertility keep changing rapidly. The census of 1911 revealed a sharp increase in the difference between the sizes of families born to labourers and to professional men, but there are hints in the census of 1951 that the difference may since have declined. There is no need to assume that professional men are innately more intelligent than labourers; the argument would be equally valid if for professional men and labourers we were to substitute the people who do or do not believe that intelligence will decline; I am saying that there has been a *change* in the habits of fertility, and that when such changes are in progress, the idea of a natural equilibrium must be set aside.

Much else could be said to the same effect. For example, it is not true that the most highly educated people are the least fertile. Apart from imbeciles and idiots, the least fertile members of our population in terms of educational standing are those whose schooling stopped short of university but went beyond what is legally required.[14] I feel that the members of this group are less fertile because they *choose* to have fewer children; I am not inclined to believe that they are either unusually intelligent or unusually stupid; so far as innate intelligence goes, they may be a perfectly fair sample of the population as a whole. Nor do I think that some subconscious premonition of infertility directs them towards occupations which they merely appear to choose. But they are a numerous class, and the least fertile; what they contribute to our understanding of a natural balance of fertility is evidence that no such balance exists.

Again, the pattern of mortality as it falls upon the large families of poorer people has changed dramatically in the past fifty years. The death-rate of children within a week or so of birth has fallen rapidly, and begins to compare with mortality in the children of the better off; but deaths during the first year of life—deaths due mainly to infectious diseases—have not yet fallen so far, and do not compare so well.[15] This is but a fragment of the evidence that must turn our thoughts away from the idea that we are in a state of equilibrium. At one time, I suppose, there may have been some natural equilibrium between intelligence and fertility—adjusted, perhaps, to an average family size of eight or ten. Perhaps matters were so adjusted that the brightest and dullest of our forebears were incapable of having families larger than four or five. But the families we have in mind today belong to the lower half of what is possible in the way of human fertility, and it is hard to believe that a new equilibrium could have grown up around families with an average size of two or three.

Let me now summarize this long and complicated argument. It is a fair assumption that a child's performance in an intelligence test—imperfect as such tests are—gives one *some* indication of its wits. It is a fact that the average performance of children in intelligence tests is related to the size of the family they belong to: the larger the number of their brothers and sisters, the lower, on the average, will be their scores. Part of this negative correlation between intelligence and size of family can be traced to causes which have no genetic implications, whether for good or ill. But differences of intelligence are strongly inherited, and in a manner which, in general terms, we think we understand. If innately unintelligent people tend to have larger families, then, with some qualifications, we can infer that the average level of intelligence will decline. There are good reasons for supposing that intelligence could not continue to decline indefinitely, but equally good reasons for thinking that it may have some way yet to go. In any event, the decline will be a slow one—much slower than the boldly negative correlation between intelligence and size of family might tempt one to suppose. All our conclusions on the matter fall very far short of certainty: there are serious weaknesses in our methods of analysis, and grave gaps in our knowledge which, it is to be hoped, someone will repair.[16]

Profound changes in habits of fertility have been taking place over the past fifty or hundred years; and they are not yet complete. The decline of intelligence (if indeed it is declining) may be a purely temporary phenomenon—a short-lived episode marking the slow transition from free reproduction accompanied by high mortality to restricted reproduction accompanied by low mortality. But even if the decline looked as if it might be long lasting, it would not be irremediable. Changes in the structure of taxation and in the award of family allowances and educational grants may already have removed some of the factors which have discouraged the more intelligent from having larger families; and in twenty-five years' time we may be laughing at our present misgivings. I do not, however, think that there is anything very much to be amused about just at present.

# 6.

## *the future of man*

In this last lecture, I shall discuss the origin in
human beings of a new, a non-genetical, system of
heredity and evolution based upon certain properties and activities of the brain. The existence of
this non-genetical system of heredity is something
you are perfectly well aware of. It was not biologists
who first revealed to an incredulous world that
human beings have brains; that having brains makes
a lot of difference; and that a man may influence
posterity by other than genetic means. Yet much of
what I have read in the writings of biologists seems
to say no more than this. I feel a biologist should
contribute something towards our *understanding* of
the distant origins of human tradition and behaviour,
and this is what I shall now attempt. The attempt
must be based upon hard thinking, as opposed to
soft thinking; I mean, it must be thinking that covers
ground and is based upon particulars, as opposed
to that which finds its outlet in the mopings or exal-
tations of poetistic prose.

It will make my argument clearer if I build it

upon an analogy. I should like you to consider an important difference between a juke-box and a gramophone—or, if you like, between a barrel-organ and a tape-recorder. A juke-box is an instrument which contains one or more gramophone records, one of which will play whatever is recorded upon it if a particular button is pressed. The act of pressing the button I shall describe as the "stimulus." The stimulus is specific: to each button there corresponds one record, and *vice versa,* so that there is a one-to-one relationship between stimulus and response. By pressing a button—any button—I am, in a sense, instructing the juke-box to play music; by pressing this button and not that, I am instructing it to play one piece of music and not another. But—I am not giving the juke-box *musical* instructions. The musical instructions are inscribed upon records that are part of the juke-box, not part of its environment: what a juke-box or barrel-organ can play on any one occasion depends upon structural or inbuilt properties of its own. I shall follow Professor Joshua Lederberg [1] in using the word "elective" to describe the relationship between what the juke-box plays and the stimulus that impinges upon it from the outside world.

Now contrast this with a gramophone or any other reproducing apparatus. I have a gramophone, and one or more records somewhere in the environment outside it. To hear a particular piece of music, I go through certain motions with switches, and put a gramophone record on. As with the juke-box I am, in a sense, instructing the gramophone to play music, and a particular piece of music. But I am doing more than that: I am giving it musical instructions, inscribed in the grooves of the record I make it play. The gramophone itself contains no source of musical information; it is the record that contains the information, but the record reached the gramophone from the outside world. My relationship to the gramophone—again following Lederberg —I shall describe as "instructive"; for, in a sense, I *taught* it what to play. With the juke-box, then— and the same goes for a musical-box or barrel-organ—the musical instructions are part of the system that responds to stimuli, and the stimuli are elective: they draw upon the inbuilt capabilities of the instrument. With a gramophone, and still more obviously with a tape recorder, the stimuli are instructive: they endow it with musical capabilities; they import into it musical information from the world outside.

It is we ourselves who have made juke-boxes and gramophones, and who decide what, if anything, they are to play. These facts are irrelevant to the analogy I have in mind, and can be forgotten from now on. Consider only the organism on the one hand—juke-box or gramophone; and, on the other hand, stimuli which impinge upon that organism from the world about it.

During the past ten years, biologists have come to realize that, by and large, organisms are very much more like juke-boxes than gramophones. Most of those reactions of organisms which we were formerly content to regard as instructive are in fact elective. The instructions an organism contains are not musical instructions inscribed in the grooves of a gramophone record, but *genetical* instructions embodied in chromosomes and nucleic acids. Let me give examples of what I mean.

The oldest example, and the most familiar, concerns the change that comes over a population of organisms when it undergoes an evolution. How should we classify the environmental stimuli that cause organisms to evolve? The Lamarckian theory, the theory that acquired characters can be inherited, is, in its most general form, an *instructive* theory of evolution. It declares that the environment can somehow issue genetical instructions to living organisms—instructions which, duly assimilated, can be passed on from one generation to the next. The blacksmith who is usually called upon to testify on these occasions gets mightily strong arms from forging; somehow this affects the cells that manufacture his spermatozoa, so that his children start life specially well able to develop strong arms. I have no time to explain our tremendous psychological inducement to believe in an instructive or Lamarckian theory of evolution, though in a somewhat more sophisticated form than this. I shall only say that every analysis of what has appeared to be a Lamarckian style of heredity has shown it to be *non*-Lamarckian.[2] So far as we know, the relationship between organism and environment in the evolutionary process is an elective relationship. The environment does *not* imprint genetical instructions upon living things.

Another example: bacteriologists have known for years that if bacteria are forced to live upon some new unfamiliar kind of foodstuff or are exposed to the action of an anti-bacterial drug, they acquire the ability to make use of that new food, or to make the drug harmless to them by breaking it down. The treatment was at one time referred to as the *training* of bacteria—with the clear implication that the new food or drug *taught* the bacteria how to manufacture the new ferments upon which their new behaviour depends. But it turns out that the process of training belies its name: it is not instructive. A bacterium can synthesize only those ferments which it is genetically entitled to synthesize. The process of training merely brings out or exploits or develops an innate potentiality of the bacterial population, a potentiality underwritten or subsidized by the particular genetic make-up of one or another of its members.[3]

The same argument probably applies to what goes on when animals develop. At one time there was great argument between "preformationists" and those who believed in epigenesis. The preformationists declared that all development was an unfolding of something already there; the older extremists, whom we now laugh at, believed that a sperm was simply a miniature man. The doctrine of epigenesis, in an equally extreme form, declared that all organisms begin in a homogeneous state, with no apparent or actual structure; and that the embryo is moulded into its adult form solely by stimuli impinging upon it from outside. The truth lies somewhere between these two extreme conceptions. The genetic instructions are preformed, in the sense that they are already there, but their fulfilment is epigenetic—an interpretation that comes close to an elective theory of embryonic development. The environment brings out potentialities present in the embryo in a way which (as with the buttons on a juke-box) is exact and discriminating and specific; but it does not *instruct* the developing embryo in the manufacture of its particular ferments or proteins or whatever else it is made of. Those instructions are already embodied in the embryo: the environment causes them to be carried out.[4]

Until a year or two ago we all felt sure that *one* kind of behaviour indulged in by higher organisms did indeed depend upon the environment as a teacher or instructor. The entry or injection of a foreign substance into the tissues of an animal brings about an immunological reaction. The organism manufactures a specific protein, an "antibody," which reacts upon the foreign substance, often in such a way as to prevent its doing harm. The formation of antibodies has a great deal to do with resistance to infectious disease. The relationship between a foreign substance and the particular antibody it evokes is exquisitely discriminating and specific; one human being can manufacture hundreds—conceivably thousands — of distinguishable antibodies, even against substances which have only recently been invented, like some of the synthetic chemicals used in industry or in the home. Is the reaction instructive or elective?—*surely,* we all felt, instructive. The organism learns from the chemical pattern of the invading substance just how a particular antibody should be assembled in an appropriate and distinctive way. Self-evident though this interpretation seems, many students of the matter are beginning to doubt it. They hold that the process of forming antibodies is probably elective in character.[5] The information which directs the synthesis of particular antibodies is part of the inbuilt genetical information of the cells that make them; the intruding foreign substance exploits that information and brings it out. It is the juke-box over again. I believe this theory is somewhere near the right one, though I do not accept some of the special constructions that have been put upon it.

So in spite of all will to believe otherwise, and for all that it seems to go against common sense, the picture we are forming of the organism is a juke-box picture—a juke-box containing genetical instructions inscribed upon chromosomes and nucleic acids in much the same kind of way as musical instructions are inscribed upon gramophone records. But what a triumph it would be if an organism could accept information from the environment—if the environment could be made to act in an instructive, not merely an elective, way! A few hundred million years ago a knowing visitor from another universe might have said: "It's a splendid idea, and I see the point of it perfectly: it would solve—or could solve—the problems of adaptation, and make it possible for organisms to evolve in a much more efficient way than by natural selection. But it's far too difficult: it simply can't be done."

But you know that it has been done, and that

there is just one organ which can accept instruction from the environment: the brain. We know very little about it, but that in itself is evidence of how immensely complicated it is. The evolution of a brain was a feat of fantastic difficulty—the most spectacular enterprise since the origin of life itself. Yet the brain began, I suppose, as a device for responding to elective stimuli. *Instinctive* behaviour is behaviour in which the environment acts electively. If male sex hormones are deliberately injected into a hen, the hen will start behaving in male-like ways. The potentiality for behaving in a male-like manner must therefore have been present in the female; and by pressing (or, as students of behaviour usually say, "releasing") the right button the environment can bring it out. But the higher parts of the brain respond to instructive stimuli: we *learn*.

Now let me carry the argument forward. It was a splendid idea to evolve into the possession of an organ that can respond to instructive stimuli, but the idea does not go far enough. If that were the whole story, we human beings might indeed live more successfully than other animals; but when we died, a new generation would have to start again from scratch. Let us go back for a moment to genetical instructions. A child at conception receives certain genetical instructions from its parents about how its growth and development are to proceed. Among these instructions there must be some which provide for the issue of further instructions; I mean, a child grows up in such a way that it, too, can eventually have children, and convey genetical instructions to them in turn. We are dealing here with a very special system of communication: a *hereditary* system. There are many examples of systems of this kind. A chain letter is perhaps the simplest: we receive a letter from a correspondent who asks us to write to a third party, asking him in turn to write a letter of the same kind to a fourth, and so on—a hereditary system. The most complicated example is provided by the human brain itself; for it does indeed act as intermediary in a hereditary system of its own. We do more than learn: we teach and hand on; tradition accumulates; we record information and wisdom in books.

Just as a hereditary system is a special kind of system of communication—one in which the instructions provide for the issue of further instructions—so there is a specially important kind of hereditary system: one in which the instructions passed on from one individual to another change in some systematic way in the course of time. A hereditary system with this property may be said to be conducting or undergoing an *evolution*. Genetic systems of heredity often transact evolutionary changes; so also does the hereditary system that is mediated through the brain. I think it is most important to distinguish between four stages in the evolution of a brain. The nervous system began, perhaps, as an organ which responded only to elective stimuli from the environment; the animal that possessed it reacted instinctively or by rote, if at all. There then arose a brain which could begin to accept instructive stimuli from the outside world; the brain in this sense has dim and hesitant beginnings going far back in geological time. The third stage, entirely distinguishable, was the evolution of a non-genetical system of heredity, founded upon the fact that the most complicated brains can do more than merely receive instructions; in one way or another they make it possible for the instructions to be handed on. The existence of this system of heredity—of tradition, in its most general sense—is a defining characteristic of human beings, and it has been important for, perhaps, 500,000 years. In the fourth stage, not clearly distinguishable from the third, there came about a systematic change in the nature of the instructions passed on from generation to generation—an evolution, therefore, and one which has been going at a great pace in the past 200 years. I shall borrow two words used for a slightly different purpose by the great demographer Alfred Lotka [6] to distinguish between the two systems of heredity enjoyed by man: *endosomatic* or internal heredity for the ordinary or genetical heredity we have in common with other animals; and *exosomatic* or external heredity for the non-genetic heredity that is peculiarly our own—the heredity that is mediated through tradition, by which I mean the transfer of information through non-genetic channels from one generation to the next.

I am, of course, saying something utterly obvious: society changes; we pass on knowledge and skills and understanding from one person to another and from one generation to the next; a man can indeed influence posterity by other than genetic means. But I wanted to put the matter in a way which shows that we must not distinguish a strictly biological evolution from a social, cultural, or technological evolution: *both* are biological evolutions: the distinction between them is that the one is genetical and the other is not.

What, then, is to be inferred from all this? What lessons are to be learned from the similarities and correspondences between the two systems of biological heredity possessed by human beings? The answer is important, and I shall now try to justify it: the answer, I believe, is almost none.

It is true that a number of amusing (but in one respect highly dangerous) parallels can be drawn between our two forms of heredity and evolution. Just as biologists speak in a kind of shorthand about the "evolution" of hearts or ears or legs—it is too clumsy and long-winded to say every time that these organs participate in evolution, or are outward expressions of the course of evolution—so we can speak of the evolution of bicycles or wireless sets or aircraft with the same qualification in mind: they do not really evolve, but they are appendages, exosomatic organs if you like, that evolve with us. And there are many correspondences between the two kinds of evolution. Both are gradual if we take the long view; but on closer inspection we shall find that novelties arise, not everywhere simultaneously —pneumatic tyres did not suddenly appear in the whole population of bicycles—but in a few members of the population: and if these novelties confer economic fitness, or fitness in some more ordinary and obvious sense, then the objects that possess them will spread through the population as a whole and become the prevailing types. In both styles of evolution we can witness an adaptive radiation, a deployment into different environments: there are wireless sets not only for the home, but for use in motor-cars of for carrying about. Some great dynasties die out—airships, for example, in common with the dinosaurs they were so often likened to; others become fixed and stable: toothbrushes retained the same design and constitution for more than a hundred years. And, no matter what the cause of it, we can see in our exosomatic appendages something equivalent to vestigial organs; how else should we describe those functionless buttons on the cuffs of men's coats?

All this sounds harmless enough: why should I have called it dangerous? The danger is that by calling attention to the similarities, which are not profound, we may forget the *differences* between our two styles of heredity and evolution; and the differences between them are indeed profound. In their hunger for synthesis and systematization, the evolutionary philosophers of the nineteenth century [7] and some of their modern counterparts have missed the point: they thought that great lessons were to be learnt from similarities between Darwinian and social evolution; but it is from the differences that all the great lessons are to be learnt. For one thing, our newer style of evolution is Lamarckian in nature. The environment cannot imprint genetical information upon us, but it can and does imprint non-genetical information which we can and do pass on. Acquired characters are indeed inherited. The blacksmith was under an illusion if he supposed that his habits of life could impress themselves upon the genetic make-up of his children; but there is no doubting his ability to teach his children his trade, so that they can grow up to be as stalwart and skilful as himself. It is because this newer evolution is so obviously Lamarckian in character that we are under psychological pressure to believe that genetical evolution must be so too. But although one or two biologists are still feebly trying to graft a Lamarckian or instructive interpretation upon ordinary genetical evolution, they are not nearly so foolish or dangerous as those who have attempted to graft a Darwinian or purely elective interpretation upon the newer, non-genetical, evolution of mankind.

The conception I have just outlined is, I think, a liberating conception. It means that we can jettison all reasoning based upon the idea that changes in society happen in the style and under the pressures of ordinary genetic evolution; abandon any idea that the direction of social change is governed by laws other than laws which have at some time been the subject of human decisions or acts of mind. That competition between one man and another is a necessary part of the texture of society; that societies are organisms which grow and must inevitably die; that division of labour within a society is akin to what we can see in colonies of insects; that the laws of genetics have an overriding authority; that social evolution has a direction forcibly imposed upon it by agencies beyond man's control—all these are biological judgments; but, I do assure you, bad judgments based upon a bad biology. In these lectures you will have noticed that I advocate a "humane" solution of the problems of eugenics, particularly of the problems of those who have been handicapped by one or another manifestation of the ineptitude of nature. I have not claimed, and do not now claim, that humaneness is an attitude of mind enforced or authorized by some deep inner law of exosomatic heredity: there are technical reasons for supposing that no such laws can exist. I am not warning you against quack biology in order to set myself up as a rival pedlar of patent medicines. What I do say is that our policies and intentions are not to be based upon the supposition that nature knows best; that we are at the mercy of natural laws, and flout them at our peril.

It is a profound truth—realized in the nineteenth century by only a handful of astute biologists and by philosophers hardly at all (indeed, most of those who held any views on the matter held a contrary opinion)—a profound truth that nature does *not* know best; that genetical evolution, if we choose to look at it liverishly instead of with fatuous good humour, is a story of waste, makeshift, compromise, and blunder.

I could give a dozen illustrations of this judgment, but shall content myself with one. You will remember my referring to the immunological defences of the body, the reactions that are set in train by the invasion of the tissues by foreign substances. Reactions of this kind are more than important: they are essential. We can be sure of this because some unfortunate children almost completely lack the biochemical aptitude for making antibodies, the defensive substances upon which so much of resistance to infectious disease depends. Until a few years ago these children died, because only antibiotics like penicillin can keep them alive; for that reason, and because the chemical methods of identifying it have only recently been discovered, the disease I am referring to was only recognized in 1952.[8] The existence of this disease confirms us in our belief that the immunological defences are vitally important; but this does not mean that they are wonders of adaptation, as they are so often supposed to be. Our immunological defences are also an important source of injury, even of mortal injury.

For example: vertebrate animals evolved into the possession of immunological defences long before the coming of mammals. Mammals are viviparous: the young are nourished for some time within the body of the mother: and this (in some ways) admirable device raised for the first time in evolution the possibility that a mother might react immunologically upon her unborn children—might treat them as foreign bodies or as foreign grafts. The haemolytic disease that occurs in about one newborn child in 150 is an error of judgment of just this kind: it is, in effect, an immunological repudiation by the mother of her unborn child. Thus the existence of immunological reactions has not been fully reconciled with viviparity; and this is a blunder —the kind of blunder which, in human affairs, calls forth a question in the House, or even a strongly worded letter to *The Times*.

But this is only a fraction of the tale of woe. Anaphylactic shock, allergy, and hypersensitivity are all aberrations or miscarriages of the immunological process. Some infectious diseases are dangerous to us not because the body fails to defend itself against them but—paradoxically—because it does defend itself: in a sense, the remedy *is* the disease. And within the past few years a new class of diseases has been identified, diseases which have it in common that the body can sometimes react upon its own constituents as if they were foreign to itself. Some diseases of the thyroid gland and some inflam-

matory diseases of nervous tissue belong to this
category; rheumatoid arthritis, lupus erythematosus,
and scleroderma may conceivably do so too.[9] I say
nothing about the accidents that used to occur in
blood transfusions, immunological accidents; nor
about the barriers, immunological barriers, that prevent our grafting skin from one person to another,
useful though it would so often be; for transfusion
and grafting are artificial processes, and, as I said
in an earlier lecture, natural evolution cannot be
reproached for failing to foresee what human beings
might get up to. All I am concerned to show is that
natural devices and dispositions are highly fallible.
The immunological defences are dedicated to the
proposition that anything foreign must be harmful;
and this formula is ground out in a totally undis-
criminating fashion with results that are sometimes
irritating, sometimes harmful, and sometimes mor-
tally harmful. It is far better to have immunological
defences than not to have them; but this does not
mean that we are to marvel at them as evidences
of a high and wise design.

We can, then, improve upon nature; but the possibility of our doing so depends, very obviously,
upon our continuing to explore into nature and to
enlarge our knowledge and understanding of what
is going on. If I were to argue the scientists' case,
the case that exploration is a wise and sensible
thing to do, I should try to convince you of it by
particular reasoning and particular examples, each
one of which could be discussed and weighed up;
some, perhaps, to be found faulty. I should not say:
Man is driven onwards by an exploratory instinct,
and can only fulfil himself and his destiny by the
ceaseless quest for Truth. As a matter of fact, animals do have what might be loosely called an in-
quisitiveness, an exploratory instinct; [10] but even if
it were highly developed and extremely powerful, it

would still not be binding upon us. We should not be *driven* to explore.

Contrariwise, if someone were to plead the virtues of an intellectually pastoral existence, not merely quiet but acquiescent, and with no more than a pensive regret for not understanding what could have been understood; then I believe I could listen to his arguments and, if they were good ones, might even be convinced. But if he were to say that this course of action or inaction was the life that was authorized by Nature; that this was the life Nature provided for and intended us to lead; then I should tell him that he had no proper conception of Nature. People who brandish naturalistic principles at us are usually up to mischief. Think only of what we have suffered from a belief in the existence and overriding authority of a fighting instinct; from the doctrines of racial superiority and the metaphysics of blood and soil; from the belief that warfare between men or classes of men or nations represents a fulfilment of historical laws. These are all excuses of one kind or another, and pretty thin excuses. The inference we can draw from an analytical study of the differences between ourselves and other animals is surely this: that the bells which toll for mankind are—most of them, anyway—like the bells on Alpine cattle; they are attached to our own necks, and it must be *our* fault if they do not make a cheerful and harmonious sound.

# *n o t e s*

## *LECTURE 1*

1. The sex-ratio in England and Wales (live births of boys per 1,000 live births of girls) rose from 1,038 in the quinquennium 1911–15 to 1,051—the highest figure that had ever been recorded—in the quinquennium 1916–20. Between 1941 and 1942 it rose from 1,053 to 1,063, reaching 1,065 in 1944. Since then the sex-ratio has centred upon 1,060. The sex-ratio normally favours males, perhaps from conception onwards; the effect of war referred to in the text is to favour males still more.

Demographical data of all kinds for England and Wales are summarized in the Registrar-General's annual *Statistical Review*, nowadays published in three parts: I, Medical; II, Civil; III, Commentary. Demographical data for the world generally are to be found in the annual *Demographic Yearbook* of the United Nations.

One comment on matters of terminology should be made without delay. Demographers use the words "fertility" and "fecundity" in the senses usually attached by biologists to "fecundity" and "fertility." I have adopted the demographic usage: "fertility," unqualified, means actual reproductive performance;

where "fecundity" or reproductive potential is intended, I use "innate fertility," or words to that effect.

2. The sex-ratio of children born in England and Wales in 1956 fell from 1,074 for children of mothers under twenty to 1,026 for children of mothers between forty and forty-four. Various fairly obvious catches prevent our taking this raw statistical observation at its face value, e.g. the facts that (*a*) a relatively high proportion of women under twenty are pregnant at marriage, so that the under-twenties may be a specially fertile group; and (*b*) the age-groupings are not equally representative of different occupational classes or different habits of birth-control, etc.

3. See, for example, J. Lejeune and R. Turpin, *C.R. Acad. Sci., Paris*, **244**, 1,833, 1957; E. Novitsky and A. W. Kimball, *Amer. J. Human Genet.*, **10**, 268, 1958. For a "physiological" rather than a demographical interpretation of the change in the sex-ratio, see T. McKeown, *Proc. 1st Int. Congr. Human Genet.*, **2**, 382, 1957.

4. The analysis referred to was carried out by J. A. Fraser Roberts, *Brit. Med. J.*, **1**, 320, 1944.

5. This deliberately vague statement is about as near as we can get to a "law" describing the actual growth of populations. The "law of increase by compound interest" or exponential law of population growth is a hypothetical statement about the consequences of combining a real rate of fertility with an imaginary rate of mortality, i.e. a mortality assumed to be independent of the population's size.

6. For a retrospective analysis of a representative number of these forecasts, see P. R. Cox, *Demography* (2nd ed., Cambridge, 1957).

7. A *gross* reproduction rate (computed for females) is roughly speaking an answer to this question: "How many new-born girls can this new-born girl be credited with, on the average, if she lives right through the

period of childbearing and has children at the average rates appropriate to each fraction of that period—rates known from current information about fertility in each age-group of the population as a whole?" The *net* reproduction rate takes into account the new-born girl's likelihood of living through the period of childbearing, and weights the estimate accordingly. From English Life Table No. 11, of 1951, only 96.3 per cent of new-born girls reach the age of twenty and only 93.8 per cent reach the age of forty. If a new-born girl can be credited, on the average, with just one new-born girl in the next generation, then the net reproduction rate is said to be unity and the population to be just holding its own. If the computational exercise is carried out for males instead of females, a different figure is arrived at; and this in itself is a source of some of the difficulties mentioned in the text.

The reorientation of our thought about the usefulness of computing reproduction rates of various kinds (there are many kinds) can be largely credited to J. Hajnal of the London School of Economics; see in particular *Population Studies*, **1**, 137, 1947–8; *Reports and Selected Papers of the Statistics Committee*, 303 (*Papers of the Royal Commission on Population*, Vol. II, London, HMSO, 1950); *1958 Annual Conf. Milbank Foundation*, p. 11 (Milbank Memorial Fund, New York). These papers contain a much more fundamental and thoroughgoing analysis than any attempted in my lecture. See also *The Determinants and Consequences of Population Trends*, United Nations, 1953.

8. The concept of "stability" and the proof that a population subject to constant age-specific mortality and fertility will eventually adopt a stable structure is the work of A. J. Lotka: see *The Elements of Physical Biology* (Baltimore, Williams & Wilkins, 1925); *Théorie analytique des Associations biologiques*, Part II (Hermann, Paris, 1939). Lotka's solution of the integral equation which yields the "true rate of natural increase" of a population has passed into the literature

of genetics, usually without acknowledgment of its source.

9. Cohort analysis was used for the first time on any large scale by D. V. Glass and E. Grebenik in their report on the Family Census of 1946 (*The Trend and Pattern of Fertility in Great Britain. Papers of the Royal Commission on Population*, Vol. VI, London, HMSO, 1954). It was also adopted in the larger and more recent *Fertility Report* on the General Census of 1951 (London, HMSO, 1959), a report which should be referred to for information on the pattern of building families. For American demographical data, see W. H. Grabill, C. V. Kiser and P. K. Whelpton, *The Fertility of American Women* (New York, Wiley, 1958).

10. It is the apocalyptic style of forecasting one should beware of. For certain special purposes forecasting is essential; to answer this question, for example: "Should our universities be expanded permanently to a size large enough to accommodate the great numbers of children born in the post-war years, or can that great number of births be treated as a temporary bulge which temporary expedients can cope with?" There's no knowing. "One future development . . . we *can* forecast with a good deal of confidence," said the Royal Commission on Population in its Report to Parliament in 1949, "namely, a substantial decline in the annual numbers of births over the next fifteen years." Actually—and quite unforeseeably—the annual number of births began to rise sharply after 1955, and forecasts of the future sizes of universities have been revised accordingly. They are sure to be revised again.

## LECTURE 2

1. Discussions about (for example) the "real" meanings of the words *living* and *dead* are felt to mark a low level in biological conversation. These words have no inner meaning which careful study will eventually disclose. Laymen use the word "dead" to mean "formerly alive"; they speak only fancifully of stones as dead and never of crystals living; but they can tell a living horse from a dead one and, what is more, can remember an apt metaphor that turns on the distinction. See N. W. Pirie, "The meaninglessness of the terms life and living" (*Perspectives in Biochemistry*, II, Cambridge, 1937).

2. The genetical usage of "fitness" is an extreme attenuation of the ordinary usage; it is, in effect, a system of *pricing* the endowments of organisms in the currency of offspring, i.e. in terms of net reproductive performance. It is a genetic valuation of goods, not a statement about their nature or quality.

3. For if medical treatment confers fitness upon the unfit, there can be no fear of extinction; if it fails to do so, the fear of extinction does not arise. The "going downhill" argument seems to contemplate the predicament of modern man in primitive surroundings, without insulin, penicillin, central heating and other allegedly debilitating devices; but it is not clear why such an exercise should be supposed to be informative.

4. This interpretation of sickle cell trait is the outcome of a brilliant combined operation between geneticists, chemists and clinicians, among them J. V. Neel, E. A. Beet, L. Pauling, V. M. Ingram and A. C. Allison. For the theory that sickle cell trait confers resistance to subtertian malaria, see A. C. Allison, *Ann. Human Genet.*, **19**, 39, 1954; for the difference between haemoglobins A and S, see V. M. Ingram, *Brit. Med. Bull.*, **15**, 27, 1957. Accounts of the genetics of sickling can be found in J. A. Fraser Roberts, *An*

*Introduction to Medical Genetics,* 2nd ed., Oxford University Press, London, 1959; H. Kalmus, *Variation and Heredity,* London, Routledge & Kegan Paul, 1957. For phenylketonuria and alkaptonuria, referred to later in the lecture, see H. Harris, *Human Biochemical Genetics* (Cambridge, 1959).

5. Cystic disease of the pancreas, the frequency of which, in Great Britain, has been put at one in 2,000 —a frequency much higher than mutation at known rates could account for. There has therefore grown up the uneasy suspicion that the carriers of the harmful gene may have, or may have had, some special advantage over normal people (see L. S. Penrose, "Mutation in Man," in *The Effect of Radiation on Human Heredity,* 101; WHO, Geneva, 1957).

Cooley's anaemia is now more generally known as thalassaemia, a form of anaemia formerly thought to be confined to the shores of the Mediterranean (hence the name). The disease has two manifestations: a milder *thalassaemai minor* in heterozygotes, i.e. those who inherit the offending gene from one parent only, and *thalassaemia major* in those (homozygotes) who inherit it from both. The frequency of thalassaemia in, for example, the Ferrara region of Italy is far higher than recurrent mutation could well account for; as with sickle cell trait, it is supposed that the heterozygotes, victims of thalassaemia minor, have had some advantage over normal people; but no one yet knows where that advantage lay. See G. Montalenti, *Atti IX Int. Congr. Genet.,* **1**, 554, 1954; J. V. Neel, *Proc. X Int. Congr. Genet.,* **1**, 108, 1959.

6. The fact that mongolism can be traced back to a particular chromosomal abnormality was discovered by J. Lejeune, M. Gauthier and R. Turpin, *C.R. Acad. Sci., Paris,* **248**, 602, 1959. Human beings have forty-six chromosomes—not, as we formerly believed, forty-eight (J. H. Tjio and A. Levan, *Hereditas,* **42**, 1, 1956; C. E. Ford and J. L. Hamerton, *Nature,* **178**, 1,020,

1956); in mongols there is an extra chromosome, apparently because one pair exists in triplicate instead of in duplicate. The newer methods of studying human chromosomes devised by C. E. Ford and his colleagues at Harwell have already led to important progress in human genetics—in particular, to the identification of the chromosomal disorders that underlie various abnormalities of sexual development.

7. For many years the nucleic acids were thought of as a kind of stuffing or padding; no one quite knew what to make of them. Our present conceptions originate with the discovery by F. Bawden and N. W. Pirie that nucleic acid is an integral part of the molecules of some plant viruses, and by O. T. Avery and his colleagues that solutions of nucleic acid can bring about a genetical transmutation in certain bacteria. A method by which genetical information can be encoded in nucleic acid was proposed by J. D. Watson and F. H. C. Crick, and their interpretation of the structure of nucleic acid is now generally accepted. The coding depends uoon the sequential pattern, down the length of the molecule, of four different pairs of organic bases; it may be likened to a Morse code with four symbols instead of two.

8. Our knowledge of the evolution of "industrial melanism" in moths derives from the work of E. B. Ford and his colleagues at Oxford.

9. See J. D. Tanner, *Growth at Adolescence* (Blackwell, Oxford, 1955). That growth rate and the rate of attainment of adolescence have been increasing is agreed upon by all parties, but a number of experts are still inclined to question the evidence which points to a secular increase in the height finally reached when growth stops. Direct information is not fully adequate; the fact that older adults are, on the average, shorter than young (but fully grown) adults might indeed be due to the fact that the older people were born before their young contemporaries and so be-

longed to an earlier and perhaps smaller generation; but it might also be due (*a*) to an actual shrinkage of individuals during their lifetimes, or (*b*) to a mortality biased against taller people, who would thus form an unrepresentatively small proportion of an older population. The balance of evidence does seem to me to turn in favour of a genuine secular increase in the heights of adults.

10. W. E. Gladstone, *Studies on Homer and the Homeric Age,* **3**, 457 (Oxford, 1858). For a general discussion of Gladstone's and other opinions on the matter, see J. André, *Etudes sur les Termes de Couleur dans la Langue Latine* (Klincksieck, Paris, 1949).

## *LECTURE 3*

1. J. A. Fraser Roberts, *An Introduction to Medical Genetics* (2nd ed., Oxford University Press, London, 1959), contains a wealth of information on Mendelian inheritance in human beings, and, in addition, an introduction to the reasoning that underlies the interpretation of metrical inheritance. In his introduction to the study of human *Variation and Heredity* (London, Routledge & Kegan Paul, 1957), H. Kalmus deals with the "genetic system" of mankind in exactly the sense intended in this lecture and the next; although I think his views on eugenics are sometimes unduly astringent (from a tendency to identify it with its worst manifestations), and although I have not been convinced by his reasoning on one or two particular points, his humanely sceptical attitude towards the excesses of what I later call *geneticism* is entirely persuasive.

2. The idea of a genetic system which may itself be the subject of evolutionary change was first impressed

upon biologists by C. D. Darlington, particularly in *The Evolution of Genetic Systems* (1st ed., Cambridge, 1939).

3. The importance of infectious diseases in the genetical transformations of mankind during the past few thousand years has been generally overlooked; for a general discussion of *Disease and Evolution,* see J. B. S. Haldane, *Ricerca Scientifica,* **19**, 3, 1949.

4. C. H. Waddington's *The Strategy of the Genes* (London, Allen & Unwin, 1957) contains the most thorough analysis yet attempted of the concepts of adaptation and adaptability.

The antithesis as I have put it—between the adaptation of an individual on the one hand, and of a population on the other—rides roughshod over a great many subtleties of the interaction between an organism and its environment; but as a first approximation to the distinction I had in mind, I think it will stand. Many biologists who have grasped the idea that it is a *population* (not a pedigree) that evolves do not yet realize that the product of evolution may also be a population—a population with a genetic structure shaped by natural selection, and with the genetical system which makes it possible for that structure to be maintained. Indeed, with free-living outbred populations the idea of a final *product* of evolution is itself misleading: such populations never stop evolving; but there are some elements in the genetic system of outbreeding organisms that could be thought of as devices for preventing too rapid a change of genetic structure in response to forces which may be purely temporary in their action.

5. The word "one" in this sentence is important. The odds are heavily against any one individual's carrying any one named harmful gene in the heterozygous state; but without doubt each one of us carries *some* such genes. Estimates of an individual's average total load of damaging or lethal recessive genes—a matter

of the utmost importance when attempting to weigh up the malign effects of radiations on mankind—range in number from three to eight: see H. M. Slatis, *Amer. J. Human Genet.*, **6**, 412, 1954; J. A. Böök, *Ann. Human Genet.*, **21**, 191, 1956; N. E. Morton, J. F. Crow and H. J. Muller, *Proc. Nat. Acad. Sci., Wash.*, **42**, 855, 1956. Paradoxically, the most rapidly lethal of these harmful genes are the least harmful or most merciful; for, in the homozygous state, they cause the death of an embryo very early in life.

6. The "classical" explanation of the depression consequent upon inbreeding runs as follows. Inbreeding leads to the fixation of genes in their homozygous forms. As luck will have it, the genes fixed in the homozygous state will sometimes be harmful or unwholesome, so that the inbred stock, if it survives at all (often it will not) will be at a disadvantage compared with wild outbred population in which harmful genes are masked by the dominance of "wild type" genes. But it is rather unlikely that the *same* harmful genes will be fixed in two different inbred lines; if we cross two such lines, therefore, each can go some way towards making good the deficiencies of the other, and the hybrid stock will be more vigorous than either of the two parental stocks from which it was derived. This explanation is plausible, and it must surely represent some part of the truth; but it is not the whole truth.

Among the "minor snags" referred to in the text is the vexatious fact that some characters sought after by breeders represent the action of genes in the heterozygous state (e.g. the blueness of blue Andalusian poultry or the roan coats of shorthorn cattle). Such characters cannot be "fixed."

7. On polymorphism generally, see E. B. Ford (e.g. *Nature*, **180**, 1,315, 1957), who has done most to clarify our thoughts about what should be properly described as polymorphism. K. Mather (*Evolution*, **9**, 52, 1955)

has explained how polymorphism might arise when two different genetic types in an interbreeding population are adapted to their environments in different ways but yet depend upon each other (as, in the simplest case, males and females do); he predicted that polymorphism might come about as a result of "disruptive" selection, and his predictions have been borne out by experiment (J. M. Thoday, *Heredity*, **13**, 187, 1959). It was R. A. Fisher, I believe, who first pointed out that polymorphism will arise when a heterozygote is favoured above the corresponding homozygotes.

Many examples of polymorphism were gathered together and discussed by J. S. Huxley in his Bateson Lecture (*Heredity*, **9**, 1, 1955). For various aspects of polymorphism in man, especially in relation to the blood groups, see the reviews by J. A. Fraser Roberts (*Brit. Med. Bull.*, **15**, 129, 1959) and P. M. Sheppard (*ibid.*, 134). That there might be some connection between disease of the thyroid and the ability or inability to taste phenylthiourea was first suggested by H. Harris, H. Kalmus and W. R. Trotter, and has since been confirmed by F. D. Kitchin, W. Howel-Evans, C. A. Clarke, R. B. McConnell and P. M. Sheppard (*Brit. Med. J.*, **1**, 1,069, 1959).

8. The superior fitness conferred by heterozygous constitutions is sometimes referred to as "heterosis" or "hybrid vigour," but agreed meanings have not yet taken firm shape. Heterosis refers (or is assumed to refer) to a superior fitness conferred by heterozygosis at *particular* genetic loci, though it is understood that many such loci may be involved when, for example, two different inbred or partially inbred stocks are crossed. On no account should the concept of hybrid vigour be extended to *human* racial crosses, or to crosses between the members of two different wild populations belonging to the same species; for here the cross is made between two outbred and heterozygous populations, each one already to some extent adapted

to its environment (see Lecture 4). For a general treatment of the problems of heterosis (including a contribution by L. S. Penrose on evidence of heterosis in man) see the proceedings of the discussion held at the Royal Society under the chairmanship of K. Mather (*Proc. Roy. Soc. B*, **144**, 143, 1956); see also a number of important publications by I. M. Lerner, of which the most recent is *The Genetic Basis of Selection*, New York, Wiley, 1958).

The idea that heterosis plays any large part in human fitness has been briskly contested by H. J. Muller (e.g. *Amer. J. Psychiatr.*, **113**, 481, 1956; *Bull. Amer. Math Soc.*, **64**, 137, 1958): heterosis, he is inclined to believe, is a temporary state of affairs to be seen only in "adaptations that have not yet stood the test of geological time." I feel he is certainly right to challenge the *mystique* which has tended to grow up around the idea that heterozygosis as such is intrinsically laudable. Where heterozygotes are the fitter organisms, it can only be because the genetic system of an organism has become adjusted to that situation. We need not suppose that the adjustment is irreversible; as Mather has pointed out, animals whose genetic system is based upon inbreeding have evidently come to terms with homozygosis, though presumably at the expense of adaptability.

9. The thoroughgoing analysis of the behaviour of metrical characters under artificial selection is the work of the past ten years; for a clear insight into the many difficult problems involved, see J. Maynard Smith, *The Theory of Evolution* (London, Penguin Books, 1958). The account given in my lecture was necessarily condensed and over-simplified. Limits to improvement may be set (*a*) by using up all the variation that is *accessible* to selection until a general shaking-up of the genetic constitution discloses patterns of genetic combination which had, until then, been obscured by linkage: see the classical paper by K. Mather and B. J. Harrison

(*Heredity*, **3**, 1, 1949); and (*b*) by using up all variation that is *amenable* to selection: for some fraction is virtually imprisoned by a greater fitness of heterozygotes. The part played by these and other factors has been the subject of intent research in the Department of Genetics, University of Birmingham; the Institute of Animal Genetics, University of Edinburgh, particularly by D. S. Falconer, E. C. Reeve, A. Robertson and F. W. Robertson; and the Department of Zoology, University College, London. I do not think it is possible to make any general statement about which of the two factors mentioned above is the more important: it will clearly depend upon the genetic system of the species under investigation. Where the number of chromosomes is large, as it is in human beings, obstinate linkages may be the less important obstacle to improvement. For an important theoretical discussion of heterosis, see A. Robertson, *J. Genet.*, **54**, 236, 1956.

10. Much of my argument can be summarized by J. M. Thoday's epigram: "The fit are those who fit their existing environments and whose descendants will fit future environments" (*A Century of Darwin*, ed. S. A. Barnett, 317; London, Heinemann, 1959). In the main, the compromise between adaptation and adaptability has been well concealed: much research in the past ten years has shown that the members of hybrid populations of outbreeding animals are *more* uniform to outward appearance and more stable in their responses to the environment than any inbred or predominantly homozygous line derived from them (see J. Maynard Smith, *op. cit.*). Inborn diversity has therefore been reconciled to outward uniformity—and to such good effect that inborn uniformity may actually lead to an outward diversity. Such a state of affairs would be entirely paradoxical if the "classical conception" referred to in the lecture were wholly true.

## LECTURE 4

1. F. Galton, *Hereditary Genius,* London, 1869. The disappearance of the noble lineages studied by Galton was perhaps too rapid to be explained merely by the hazard of random extinction.

2. See C. D. Darlington, *Nature,* 182, 14, 1958. As to taxation, I have been told that the structure of taxation in the Netherlands is such as to make marriage an alternative to destitution; but in this country there is a definite fiscal inducement to live in sin.

3. Human beings in sparsely populated agricultural or pastoral communities tend to form little genetic pools ("isolates") between which apparently capricious differences of genetic make-up may arise ("drift"): see, for example, B. Glass, *Amer. J. Phys. Anthropol.,* 14, 451, 1956.

G. Dahlberg (*Genetics,* 14, 421, 1929) was the first to try to estimate the numerical sizes of human genetic isolates and to answer the question "from how large a number of women, on the average, does a man choose his wife?" His methods (enterprising but somewhat unsound: see N. E. Morton, *Ann. Eugen.,* 20, 116, 1955 gave a figure of the order of hundreds; more recent computations relying upon the same principle put the order of magnitude at thousands; at all events it is not a matter of tens of thousands, as optimistic young men may be tempted to assume. Geneticists with leanings towards anthropology are more interested nowadays in the spatial sizes of isolates: see the amusing analysis by L. Cavalli-Sforza (*Proc. Xth Int. Cong. Genet.,* 1, 389, 1959) of the parish registers of the diocese of Parma, which contains some 300,000 souls engaged mainly in agricultural pursuits. There turns out to be a surprisingly regular relationship between the likelihood of marriage and the distance apart of the dwelling places of the future bride and groom. The relationship fits neatly with the hypothesis (fortunately unknown to

Isaac Newton, whose metaphysical tendencies gained ground in his later years) that the attractive power of a person living at a distance $r$ from a community of population-mass $N$ is directly proportional to $N$ and inversely proportional to the square of $r$. Sociologists have published several such analyses: J. H. S. Bossard (*Amer. J. Sociol.*, 38, 219, 1932) classified 5,000 successive marriage licentiates in Philadelphia and found that more than half the bridegrooms lived within twenty blocks of their future brides; less than one-fifth lived in different cities.

4. For the fingerprints of Jews, see L. Sachs and M. Bat-Miriam, *Amer. J. Human Genet.*, 9, 117, 1957. Infantile (not juvenile) amaurotic idiocy and pentosuria are far commoner in Jews than Gentiles, but cases of phenylketonuria among Jews are very rare.

The tendency of deaf-mutes to marry one another is one of the less familiar examples of assortative mating; their need for special training brings them together, and, beyond that, they have a special understanding of and sympathy for each other's needs. Assortative mating is said to have been not uncommon among albinos or dwarfs in the days when their exhibition in circus side-shows threw them together more often than would have come about by chance.

5. For the theory underlying the higher expectation of "recessive diseases" among the children of marriages between first cousins, see J. A. Fraser Roberts or H. Kalmus, *op. cit.* The phenomenon was well known to Sir Archibald Garrod, who called attention to the greater frequency of alkaptonuria among the children of cousin marriages. Much genetical use has been made of the fact that, in the Roman Catholic Church, cousin marriages can take place only by a recorded dispensation.

C. H. Allström (*Acta Genet. Statis. Med.*, 8, 295, 1958) undertook a particularly thorough analysis of cousin marriages in Sweden. Marriages between first cousins were unconditionally forbidden until 1750; from then until 1844 they were allowed only by Royal dispensation, and each such dispensation was recorded. The frequency of cousin marriages in Sweden has not declined very greatly since then, and in some parts of Europe (e.g. Southern Italy, including Sicily) it seems to have risen.

6. J. B. S. Haldane and H. J. Muller are fond of pointing out the special contribution short-sighted people may have made to the welfare of primitive communities. The principle I mention is of fundamental importance and deserved a more serious-minded illustration. Various aspects of the matter have been discussed by R. F. Ewer (*New Biology,* **13**, 117, 1952); W. H. Thorpe (*J. An. Ecol.,* **14**, 67, 1945); E. Schrödinger (*Mind and Matter,* Cambridge, 1958); and C. H. Waddington (*Nature,* **183**, 1,634, 1959). "An animal by its behaviour," Waddington points out, "contributes in a most important way to determining the nature and intensity of the selective pressures which will be exerted on it."

7. The identification of the carriers of harmful recessive genes has made progress in recent years: see D. Y.-Y. Hsia, *Genetics,* **9**, 98, 1957. For example, the carriers of the gene which (when inherited from both parents) is responsible for phenylketonuria can now be identified with fair accuracy: they are less well able than normal people to break down phenylalanine. About one-quarter of the children of a marriage between two such heterozygotes will be afflicted by phenylketonuria. One day, perhaps, people will be "typed" for some of the harmful recessive genes they carry as often and as readily as they are nowadays grouped by the properties of their blood, and two carriers of the gene for phenylketonuria might well be warned of the possible consequences of their having children. "Marriage counselling" of this kind seems both sensible and humane, but two qualifications should

be borne in mind. (*a*) Any reduction in the incidence of phenylketonuria that may be brought about by discouraging marriages between heterozygotes will be eugenic in a symptomatic sense, for it will in fact reduce the frequency of phenylketonuria; but it will not, of course, decrease the frequency of the offending gene. On the contrary, the frequency will rise, because natural selection (presumably exercised only against the overt sufferers, homozygotes) will be proportionately relaxed. See the discussion by J. Maynard Smith, *op. cit.,* pp. 302–5. (*b*). A reduction in the number of victims of phenylketonuria may, for want of subjects to investigate, postpone the discovery of a cure. This second point may be insubstantial, but I mention both to emphasize the fact that eugenics is by no means plain sailing, and that symptomatic and radical eugenics may sometimes be at cross purposes with each other.

8. C. H. Waddington expounds his important concept of *genetic assimilation* in *The Strategy of the Genes* (London, Allen & Unwin, 1957), and explains the Darwinian basis of ostensibly Lamarckian patterns of inheritance.

9. See, for example, I. M. Lerner, *The Genetic Basis of Selection,* pp. 20–1 (New York, Wiley, 1958). It must be clearly understood that the word *gene* stands for a genetic, not a structural concept: a gene is known by its performance and not by its substantive properties. There is no *a priori* reason why the structural entity revealed by mutation should coincide exactly with that which is revealed by crossing over or by the exercise of a particular physiological action; see the particularly cogent analysis by G. Pontecorvo, *Trends in Genetic Analysis* (Oxford University Press, 1959). I suppose that the genetical definition of the units of inheritance will ultimately be superseded by a structural or molecular definition.

The systematic analysis of polygenic inheritance in the quantal language of Mendelian genetics is particularly associated with the name of K. Mather (*Biometrical Genetics*: London, Methuen, 1949).

10. Here see H. Spurway, *J. Genet.*, **53**, 325, 1955. I cannot help feeling that some element of the tameness or docility of domesticated animals (e.g. sheep and cattle) is the product of selection for frank mental deficiency; and I wonder how tame rats compare for intelligence with wild rats.

11. A certain genealogist, hungry for "scientific" evidence to justify the belief that the male line of descent is specially meritorious, swallowed the naïve belief that the Y-chromosome (which travels down the male line) contains the genetic determinants of virility. His reasoning is akin to that which is alleged to have induced Russian soldiers to steal electric light switches from German homes in order that they, too, should have electric light when they returned home. The sex chromosomes act essentially as switches which direct development into alternative pathways. The genetic importance of the Y-chromosome as such varies from species to species—trivial, apparently, in fruit flies, though the study of various sexual anomalies shows that it has some importance in its own right in man (see *Lancet,* **1**, 715, 1959). In fish, judicious experiments on selection have made it possible to shift the burden of sex-determination to chromosomes other than the "sex" chromosomes.

12. Cohort analysis (see Lecture 1) makes it possible to work out what fraction of a whole family is completed in each year after the parents' marriage or the mother's birth. In this country (if we disregard the interruptions caused by two wars) there has been a slow progressive decline in the mean age at marriage and a slow increase in the proportion of the family completed by the fifth or tenth year after marriage. Facts and figures are to be found in the demographic documents referred to in the Notes to Lecture 1. In this country those who married between 1900 and 1909 had

47 per cent of all their children within five years of marriage, and 74 per cent within ten. The corresponding figures for the "marriage cohort" of 1925 were 55 per cent and 81 per cent respectively. In 1935, 57 per cent of all (first) marriages were contracted below twenty-five; in 1950, 70 per cent. The mean age at marriage (all the figures I quote are, of course, averages) fell by just over a year, for both men and women, between 1946 and 1955. There has, then, been a tendency towards an earlier completion of families; family limitation might have taken the form of a postponement of childbearing, but in this country it has not done so.

13. A decline in the incidence of mongolian idiocy follows directly from L. S. Penrose's demonstration that its frequency rises sharply with maternal age.

An interesting and up-to-date analysis of the frequency of monozygotic and dizygotic twinning as a function of maternal age is to be found in Part III of the Registrar-General's annual *Statistical Review* for 1956 (London, HMSO). As to the point about sex-ratio, the Registrar-General's figures for the number of men per 1,000 women in the population of England and Wales in 1956 are as follows: age group 0–4, 1,052; 20–4, 1,027; 30–4, 996; 40–4, 970.

14. The form of cancer I refer to is that which often develops from (familial) intestinal polyposis. The inheritance of Huntington's chorea (for recent genetical investigations, see E. T. Reed and J. H. Chandler, *Amer. J. Human Genet.*, **10**, 201, 1958) is governed by a gene with a strong expression in the heterozygous state; the mean age of onset for both men and women has been put at thirty-five. Many years ago, G. Levit (*C.R. Acad. Sci. URSS*, **2**, 502, 1935) pointed out that genes such as those responsible for Huntington's chorea may be classified as recessive in expression for the first part of life and dominant thereafter; and that the expected evolution towards recessiveness has, in this case,

taken the form of a postponement of the overt action of the gene. Some of the wider implications of this phenomenon have been discussed by L. S. Penrose (*Amer. J. Mental Deficiency,* 46, 453, 1942) and by myself (*The Uniqueness of the Individual,* Methuen, London, 1957). If there are inherited differences in the ages of onset of Huntington's chorea and other diseases of somewhat late expression, the action of natural selection must be to postpone their appearance. At one time it was believed that diseases of this kind made their appearance earlier and earlier in life in each successive generation—Nature's way, we were assured, of ridding herself of the genetic incubus, for eventually the victims would be afflicted too early to breed. The concept of "anticipation" (as the phenomenon is called: echoes of it remain in the term *dementia praecox*) has been completely discredited: see A. Lewis's Galton Lecture, *Eugen. Rev.,* 50, 91, 1958.

15. The source of nearly all our actuarial knowledge of rotifers is A. I. Lansing: see A. Comfort, *The Biology of Senescence,* London, Routledge & Kegan Paul, 1956.

16. The phenomenon I refer to here is far from obvious, and a word of technical explanation is called for. Consider a recessive gene $a$ of frequency $p$ which in homozygous form causes death at age one. After one generation of random mating, the frequencies of the genetypes $aa$, $Aa$ and $AA$ will be in the ratio $p^2:2pq:q^2$ where $q = 1 - p$. The fraction $p^2$ will die, and the frequency of $a$ in the residual population will therefore fall from $p$ to $pq/(2pq + q^2)$. But if the members of the population are having fewer children than they could have had, they are in a position to replace the lost fraction $p^2$ of homozygotes by normal children of genotypes $Aa$ or $AA$. The homozygotes, *ex hypothesi*, can arise only from marriages between heterozygotes $(Aa \times Aa)$, from which it follows that two-thirds of the deficit $p^2$ will be made up by children of genotype

*Aa,* and one-third by children of genotype *AA.* The frequencies of genotypes *Aa* and *AA* in the surviving population will now therefore be $2pq+\frac{2}{3}p^2$ and $q^2+\frac{1}{3}p^2$ respectively; in other words, the frequency of *a* will now drop to only $pq+\frac{1}{3}p^2$. In fact, of course, *a* will be constantly reintroduced into the population by mutation, and a new equilibrium will be established in which *a* occurs with a frequency $p'$ slightly higher than $p$. The effect at best (or at worst) is trivial; but it might introduce yet another source of error into the "indirect" method of computing mutation rates of recessive genes.

"Replacement," or compensation for lost children, is a real enough phenomenon: it may even amount to over-compensation (R. R. Race, *Ann. Eugen.,* **11**, 365, 1942). It applies not merely to a genetic situation of the kind described above, but also to the loss of children as a result of haemolytic disease (B. Glass, *Amer. J. Human Genet.,* **2**, 269, 1950). For a thorough formal analysis of the phenomenon, consult C. C. Li, *Amer. Nat.,* **87**, 257, 1953; R. C. Lewontin, *ibid.,* 375

## LECTURE 5

1. The distribution of scores in intelligence tests is, to a good approximation, normal (Gaussian): see J. A. Fraser Roberts on "The Genetics of Oligophrenia," *Congr. Int. Psychiatrie,* pp. 55–117 (Paris, Hermann, 1950). Fraser Roberts points out that whereas the feeble-minded form part of the lower end of the normal distribution of intelligence, idiots and imbeciles form a group that lies outside it.

2. For the history of popular attitudes towards fertility and mental abnormality, see A. Lewis, *Eugen. Rev.*, **50**, 91, 1958.

3. The case for a decline in the average level of intelligence, based upon the negative correlation between intelligence and size of family, is argued by C. Burt, *Intelligence and Fertility* (Occasional Papers on Eugenics, No. 2: London, Eugenics Society, 1952), and G. Thomson, *The Trend of National Intelligence* (*ibid.*, No. 3, 1947). See also the memorandum by Thomson and the discussion arising out of it in Vol. V of the *Papers of the Royal Commission on Population* (London, HMSO, 1950). Most estimates of the magnitude of the correlation between intelligence and size of family put it between −0.2 and −0.3: see the admirable review by J. D. Nisbet, *Family Environment* (Occasional Papers on Eugenics, No. 8: London, Eugenics Society, 1953) and the discussion by A. Anastasi, *Psychol. Bull.*, **53**, 187, 1956. A particularly careful analytical study of intelligence and family size was carried out by J. A. Fraser Roberts, R. M. Norman and R. Griffiths in the third of five important *Studies on a Child Population in Bath* (*Ann. Eugen.*, **8**, 178, 1938).

The case for a decline of intelligence is no longer built upon demographic evidence that manual labourers, particularly unskilled labourers, are more prolific than scholars, administrators and clerks: the facts are clear enough, but the inferences that used to be drawn from them are highly dubious. Nevertheless the illusion still persists that anyone who entertains the idea that intelligence may be declining is conniving at a fascist plot to discredit the working classes. Those who still hold this simple-minded view will be surprised by the temperateness of Thomson's and Burt's reasoning; but temperate though it may be, it is not free from genetical naivetes—notably Burt's belief that the aptitudes revealed by intelligence tests are "inborn" and virtually uninfluenced by upbringing and environment, and Thomson's unawareness (understandable enough) of newer developments in the study of metrical inheritance.

4. See. J. A. Fraser Roberts, *Brit. J. Psychol.* (Statistical Section), October 1947, p. 35.

5. The argument here is J. D. Nisbet's, *op. cit.*

6. See J. D. Turner, *Growth at Adolescence* (Oxford, Blackwell, 1955).

7. For a cogent discussion of the theory underlying the attempt to discriminate between genetic and environmental influences, see L. Hogben, *Nature and Nurture* (London, Allen & Unwin, 1945).

8. Not all geneticists use the word "additive" in quite this sense: some confine it to interactions between alleles at different loci.

9. *The Trend of Scottish Intelligence*, Publ. Scottish Council for Research in Education, XXX (University of London Press, 1949). For the style of test used in 1947, see L. A. Terman and M. Merrill, *Measuring Intelligence* (London, Harrap, 1937).

10. The figure I mention—1½ inches—is arrived at by interpolation between two figures given to the Scottish Council by the Education Health Service of Glasgow: over the period 1932–47, the average height of nine-year-olds increased by 1.3 inches and of thirteen-year-olds by 1.7 inches: see *Social Implications of the 1947 Scottish Mental Survey*, Publ. Scottish Council for Research in Education, XXXV (University of London Press, 1953), the authors of which find it hard to believe that so great an increase of height (with all that it implies of better up-bringing) should not be associated with an improved performance in intelligence tests. Dr. J. M. Tanner has made the same point.

11. See L. S. Penrose, *Lancet*, **2**, 425, 1950; *Brit. J. Psychol.*, **40**, 128, 1950; *Proc. Roy. Soc.*, B 144, 203, 1955. Everyone is indebted to Penrose for importing some of the newer concepts of metrical inheritance

and heterosis into the reasoning of educationalists and psychologists, but I disagree with his belief that the population of Great Britain can be supposed to be in a state of natural balance or genetic equilibrium. Human geneticists are fond of pointing out that human beings are a genetically "wild" population. One of the greatest handicaps to the genetical analysis of wild populations is the difficulty of obtaining reliable evidence about natural fertility and habits of mating. But there is a wealth of information of just this kind about human populations: if it exists, why not use it? That demographers and geneticists seem to live in worlds of their own is a puzzling anomaly.

12. See Lecture 3.

13. *Report of an Enquiry into Family Limitation by* E. Lewis-Faning; Papers of the Royal Commission on Population, Vol. I, London, HMSO, 1949.

14. See the *Fertility Report* (London, HMSO, 1959) on the General Census of 1951, particularly Table 3.4, p. xlix; the analysis is, of course, out of date, because it turns on a comparison between the family sizes of women aged forty-five to forty-nine at census and the family sizes of all women under fifty. There are hints from America that college-educated women now plan to have larger families than the less well educated: R. Freedman, P. K. Whelpton and A. A. Campbell, *Family Planning, Sterility and Population Growth* (New York, McGraw Hill, 1959).

15. These remarks should be qualified by more recent evidence: see J. N. Morris, *Lancet*, **1**, 303, 1959.

16. E. Hutchinson (*Amer. Nat.*, **93**, 81, 1959) has raised a problem which has several points in common with the one discussed here. It is a fair guess that there is some genetic element in abnormal sexual preferences or behaviour ("paraphilia," e.g. homosexuality), and that paraphilia is associated with some degree of infertility. How comes it, then, that paraphilia should

not have been almost totally extinguished by the strong selection against it? Hutchinson inclines towards an explanation cognate with Penrose's (note 11 above): perhaps the most fertile people have a predominantly heterozygous make-up with respect to genetic factors affecting sexual behaviour; and perhaps paraphilia of one kind or another is the distinguishing mark of a mainly homozygous tail of the distribution of genotypes to be expected in the offspring of marriages between such heterozygotes. It will be many years before we can decide whether or not there is an element of truth in this interpretation. See also A. Comfort, *ibid.*, 389.

## *LECTURE 6*

1. See J. Lederberg, *J. Cell. Comp. Physiol.*, suppl. 1, 52, 398, 1958. It should not be necessary to say that a distinction such as that proposed by Lederberg can be apt and informative without claiming to hold good for all time or to be unconditionally valid at all levels of analysis. Nor should it be necessary to point out that the analogy of juke-box versus gramophone is intended to do no more than guide the reader's thoughts towards the sense of the distinction.

2. Reviews by J. S. Huxley, *Evolutions: the Modern Synthesis* (London, Allen & Unwin, 1942); P. B. Medawar, *The Uniqueness of the Individual* (London, Methuen, 1957).

3. The phenomenon described here should be distinguished from the evolution of resistant bacterial strains (see Lecture 2). The power of an *individual* bacterium to develop any particular "adaptive enzyme" in response to a particular inductive stimulus depends

upon its genetic constitution: the action of the "inducer" is elective. Superimposed upon this phenomenon is the selection of those bacteria, among the population as a whole, which have the genetic constitution that enables them to respond in this way. It was this second phenomenon I referred to in Lecture 2.

4. The words "evocator," "releaser" and "inductor," used by embryologists, students of behaviour and bacteriologists respectively, all have the connotation of *elective* action in Lederberg's terminology. For some discussion of the embryological problem, see my "Postscript" to *D'Arcy Wentworth Thompson*, by Ruth D'Arcy Thompson (Oxford University Press, 1958).

5. The "elective" theory of antibody formation was the bold innovation of F. M. Burnet: see *The Clonal Selection Theory of Acquired Immunity*, Cambridge, 1959. One of the great problems confronting an elective theory is this: does the zygote from which an adult arises already contain enough genetical information to underwrite the synthesis of all the antibodies an adult is capable of forming? Or must we suppose that new genetical information comes into being during the course of development? Burnet inclines towards the latter interpretation, and in its present form his theory proposes that particular lineages of antibody-forming cells are qualified to produce only one kind of antibody. This, however, is only one construction that can be put upon an elective theory of antibody formation.

6. See A. J. Lotka, *Human Biol.*, **17**, 167, 1945. Lotka was thinking in particular of the "evolution" of sensory and motor adjuncts: see my article on "Tradition: the Evidence of Biology," in *The Uniqueness of the Individual*. I am extending it here to include cultural or social evolution in the wider sense envisaged by J. S. Huxley and C. H. Waddington.

7. See, for example, Karl Pearson's *The Grammar of Science* (1892). Pearson was a humane man, and he struggles against what he believes to be the inescapable

social implications of Darwinism; he could hardly bring himself to stomach the social Darwinism of, for example, Haeckel ("The theory of selection teaches us that in human life, exactly as in animal and plant life, at each place and time only a small privileged minority can continue to exist and flourish; the great mass must starve and more or less prematurely perish in misery. . . . We may deeply mourn this tragic fact, but we cannot deny or alter it!" The exclamation mark is mine).

8. The disease is agammaglobulinaemia or, better, hypogammaglobulinaemia. Most antibodies belong to the missing or almost missing gamma-globulin fraction of blood protein. See O. A. Bruton, *Pediatrics*, **9**, 722, 1952.

9. The study of "auto-immunity" and of auto-immune diseases has been particularly associated in recent years with the names of J. Freund and E. Witebsky. That Hashimoto's thyroiditis is essentially the consequence of a self-immunization was demonstrated by I. M. Roitt and D. Doniach. For a general review of these matters, see B. H. Waksman, *Experimental Allergic Encephalomyelitis and the Auto-Allergic Diseases* (Basel, Karger, 1959).

10. Discussed by S. A. Barnett, *Brit. J. Psychol.*, **49**, 289, 1958.

# MENTOR Books on Evolution and Biology

**The Origin of Species** *by Charles Darwin.* The classic work on man's evolution, that revolutionized the scientific and religious thinking from the 19th century onwards.
(#MT294—75¢)

**Man in the Modern World** *by Julian Huxley.* Stimulating essays on vital issues from Huxley's "Man Stands Alone" and "On Living in a Revolution."   (#MD148—50¢)

**Heredity, Race and Society** (revised) *by L. C. Dunn and Th. Dobzhansky.* Group differences, how they arise, the influences of heredity and environment.   (#MD74—50¢)

**Man: His First Million Years** *by Ashley Montagu.* A vivid, lively account of the origin of man and the development of his races, cultures, customs and beliefs. (#MD239—50¢)

**The Wellsprings of Life** *by Isaac Asimov.* A fascinating introduction to the chemistry of living cells.
(#MT322—50¢)

**The Next Development in Man** (revised) *by Lancelot Law Whyte.* Art, politics, economics and science are integrated into a "unitary" way of thinking in this stimulating book.
(#MD327—50¢)

**Man Makes Himself** *by V. Gordon Childe.* Man's social and technical evolution through 340,000 years of progress.
(#MD154—50¢)

**Mainsprings of Civilization** *by Ellsworth Huntington.* A penetrating analysis of how climate, weather, geography, and heredity determine a nation's character and history. Diagrams, maps, tables, bibliography.   (#MT248—75¢)

**The Sea Around Us** *by Rachel L. Carson.* An outstanding best-seller and National Book Award winner, an enthralling account of the ocean and its inhabitants. (#MD272—50¢)

# MENTOR Philosophers of Interest

**The Limitations of Science** *by J. W. N. Sullivan*. The boundaries and potentialities of present-day scientific concepts, explained in layman's language. (#MD35—50¢)

**Knowledge, Morality, and Destiny** (New Bottles for New Wine) *by Julian Huxley*. A provocative view of man's hopeful future. (#MD303—50¢)

**Adventures of Ideas** *by Alfred North Whitehead*. By one of the outstanding philosophers of our time, a brilliant history of mankind's great thoughts which traces the development of crucial ideas from ancient times to the present. (#MD141—50¢)

**The Age of Reason: The 17th Century Philosophers** *edited by Stuart Hampshire*. "His (Hampshire's) book is a most satisfying addition to an excellent series."—*Saturday Review* (#MD158)

**The Age of Enlightenment: The 18th Century Philosophers** *edited by Sir Isaiah Berlin*. "(Sir Isaiah) has one of the liveliest and most stimulating minds among contemporary philosophers."—*N. Y. Herald Tribune* (#MD172—50¢)

**The Age of Ideology: The 19th Century Philosophers** *edited by Henry D. Aiken*. ". . . perhaps the most distinct intellectual contribution made in the series."—*New York Times* (#MD185—50¢)

**The Age of Analysis: 20th Century Philosophers** *edited by Morton White*. "No other book remotely rivals this as the best available introduction to 20th century philosophy." —*N. Y. Herald Tribune* (#MT353—75¢)

To Our Readers: We welcome your request for our free catalog of SIGNET and MENTOR Books. If your dealer does not have the books you want, you may order them by mail enclosing the list price plus 5¢ a copy to cover mailing. The New American Library of World Literature, Inc., P. O. Box 2310, Grand Central Station, New York 17, N. Y.

# How To Build
# A Low-Cost Library

*You can build a personal library of the best books for as little as 35 or 50 cents a volume. Choose from thousands of the classics and best sellers in literature, biography, poetry, art, history, religion, reference, and science as listed in a new catalog:*

## Paperbound Books in Print

If you've often had trouble finding the paperbacks you want—here are over 13,000—with information on how and where to get them. Here you can locate all the low-priced paper books available either by checking the thousands of titles listed alphabetically by author and by title, or by looking under any of the 90 categories where selected titles are grouped under helpful subject classification.

*Order* your copy of this unique buying guide today—either from your dealer or direct from RRB, New American Library of World Literature, 501 Madison Avenue, New York 22, N. Y.

*If you order from New American Library please make checks payable to: R. R. Bowker Company. Single copies are $2 net prepaid, or you can subscribe to the 4 quarterly issues for just $6 a year and automatically be kept up to date on available paperbacks.*